9

365 BRIAN THE BEAR ADVENTURES

365 Brian the Bear Adventures Bedtime stories

© 1994 Rebo Productions, Lisse
© 1996 Published by Rebo Productions Ltd

Text:
Maan Jansen

Illustrations:
Maan Jansen

Cover design:
Ton Wienbelt, The Netherlands

Production:
TextCase, The Netherlands

Translation:
*David Kennard for First Edition Translations Ltd,
Great Britain*

Typesetting:
*Computech for First Edition Translations Ltd,
Great Britain*

ISBN 1 901094 02 2

MAAN JANSEN

365 BRIAN THE BEAR ADVENTURES

REBO PRODUCTIONS

1 January

Brian

It's time to meet a very large and very lovable bear. "My name is Brian," he says, with a huge smile on his face, "and I live in the forest with all the other animals." Brian knows *everyone* who lives in the forest, he's such a friendly bear. Maybe he's not the cleverest bear in the world. Sometimes he finds things difficult to understand, and his brain works rather slowly. But bears aren't supposed to be *too* clever. At least that's what his mother always tells him, and she should know. Brian thinks that mother bears are always right. Except, of course, when they forget things. Perhaps she has done this once or twice, but Brian never noticed.

2 January

Honey

"What a beautiful day," thinks Brian, as he strolls through the forest. The sun is shining, the birds are singing, and the flowers are smiling as Brian passes by. Brian loves going for walks, even when it's raining. Did you know that bears don't mind getting wet? A brisk shake and the water flies off their fur like a heavy shower of rain. In fact, bears think water is great fun. Brian loves splashing around in the river. "But not today," thinks Brian. Brian has got honey on his mind because he's feeling hungry.

3 January

On the way

Brian scratches his head as he tries to remember where to find some honey. "Bother!" he mutters, as his stomach starts to rumble. "Why didn't I listen to my mother when she told me." Then at last he remembers. "You must pay a visit to the bees at the edge of the forest if you want to find some honey." Brian sets off happily along the path that leads to the edge of the forest. He picks a blade of grass on the way and chews it carefully. "That was nice," he says, "but it's not enough to feed a hungry bear. I must have some honey!" Soon he passes a tall fir tree. Whenever he sees this tree his shoulders start to itch. He knows he *has* to rub his back against its bark. "Oooh! That's lovely," he purrs in a beary voice, as he scratches his back against the tree.

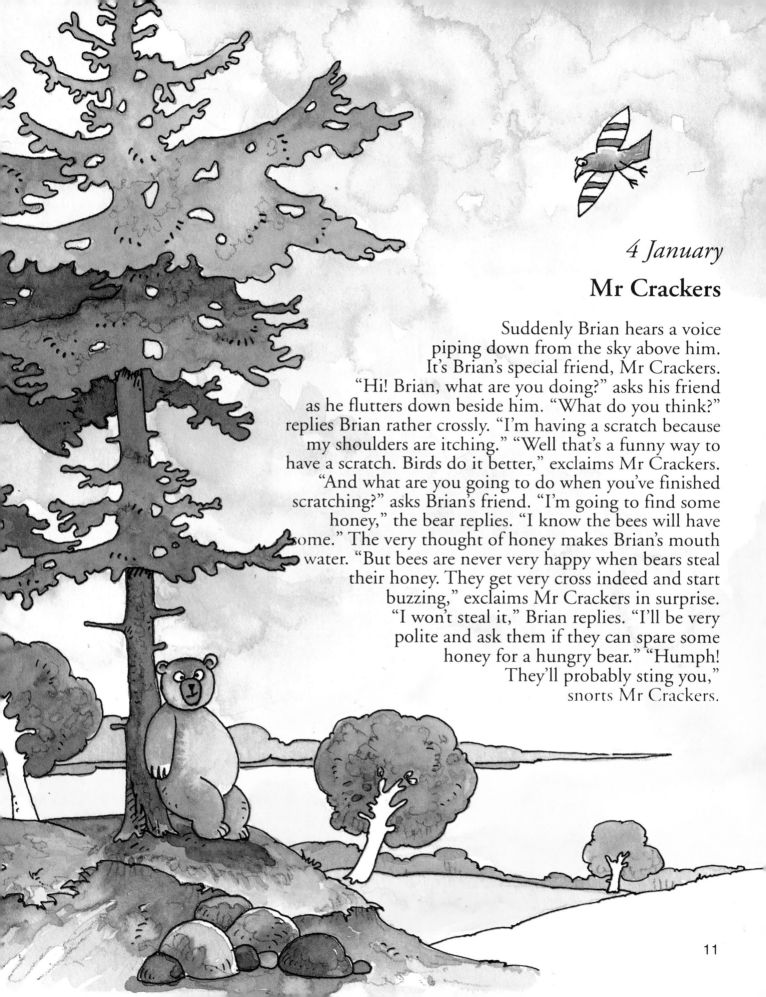

4 January

Mr Crackers

Suddenly Brian hears a voice
piping down from the sky above him.
It's Brian's special friend, Mr Crackers.
"Hi! Brian, what are you doing?" asks his friend
as he flutters down beside him. "What do you think?"
replies Brian rather crossly. "I'm having a scratch because
my shoulders are itching." "Well that's a funny way to
have a scratch. Birds do it better," exclaims Mr Crackers.
"And what are you going to do when you've finished
scratching?" asks Brian's friend. "I'm going to find some
honey," the bear replies. "I know the bees will have
some." The very thought of honey makes Brian's mouth
water. "But bees are never very happy when bears steal
their honey. They get very cross indeed and start
buzzing," exclaims Mr Crackers in surprise.
"I won't steal it," Brian replies. "I'll be very
polite and ask them if they can spare some
honey for a hungry bear." "Humph!
They'll probably sting you,"
snorts Mr Crackers.

11

5 January

Sticking together

Brian's mind is made up. He's determined to ask the bees for some honey. So with a purposeful expression on his face, he strides down the path towards the edge of the forest. Mr Crackers doesn't want to let his friend go off on his own, he thinks it's far too dangerous. "Hang on a moment," he gulps, catching his breath as he flies off after Brian. "You need all the friends you've got at a time like this, I'm coming with you." And with these words, he lands, with a graceful bow, on Brian's shoulder. He always sits on Brian's shoulder when they go for a walk. It makes it so much easier for them to talk, and Mr Crackers finds it very comfortable. Mr Crackers is really worried about his friend. "Asking the bees for honey? It's a mad idea," thinks Mr Crackers. "It can only lead to trouble." But he holds his tongue. He knows Brian won't listen to him. Bears can be very stubborn.

6 January

High up!

At last they reach a tall tree at the edge of the forest. Brian looks up. The bees' nest is hanging from a long thin branch. "It's very high up!" warns Mr Crackers, who has flown up to the top of the tree and is waiting to see what happens next. "Hmm," growls Brian, huffily. "Do you think I'm too frightened to climb a tree? We'll see about that!"

7 January

A little rest

Brian starts to climb the tree. About half way up, he has to stop for a moment. "Oh dear, this is hard going," he says to himself, as he catches his breath. "What, are you tired already?" teases Mr Crackers. "Of course not!" pants Brian. "I'm just having a little rest. There's no hurry." Bravely he hauls himself higher into the tree. Oh dear, the branches are getting thinner and Brian begins to wobble dangerously. He even has to shut his eyes to stop himself feeling dizzy. Slowly he starts to crawl along the branch towards the bees' nest. Bzzz. Bzzzzz! Brian looks around nervously. He can feel some bees buzzing round his ears and they don't look friendly. "What are you doing here?" the chief bee demands rudely.

8 January

Bees

"I've come to ask you if you can spare me some honey," mumbles Brian. "I thought you might be kind enough to give me some because I'm ever so hungry." "Did you indeed?" buzz the bees. "What makes you think we've got honey to spare? It's our store for the winter." Brian begins to move gingerly along the branch. "Stop that at once, or I'll sting you!" threatens the chief bee. Brian moves backwards with a start, and the branch begins to sway wildly. He tries to hold on tight, but it is no use. "Aaargh!" cries Brian as he falls out of the tree. Mr Crackers is laughing so much, he topples off his branch, too. "It's a good thing birds can fly," he chuckles.

9 January

Sherman

Brian is sitting on the ground feeling rather dazed and battered. "Perhaps it wasn't such a good idea to ask the bees for honey. Mr Crackers was right when he warned me not to climb that tree," thinks Brian, blushing with embarrassment. "What's going on?" asks a voice suddenly. It's Sherman the sheep, who happens to be passing by. "Don't you know that bears can't fly," he baas cheekily.

10 January

A stupid thing to do

"I think I fell out the tree," stutters Brian. He's still feeling rather confused because he hit the ground with a mighty thump. "What do you mean *you think*? I know that's what happened!" baas Sherman. "What I mean is ..." but Brian is not at all sure what he does mean. "That silly sheep is always around whenever something like this happens," grumbles Brian. "Now the whole forest will find out that I've done something stupid again."

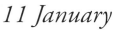

11 January

A quarrel

"Well, I don't think sheep are all that clever," interrupts Mr Crackers, taking his friend's side in the argument. "I can remember when *you* tripped over a mole hill because you weren't looking where you were going." Mr Crackers plucks a feather from his tail thoughtfully. "You spent three weeks hobbling around on sore feet," continues Mr Crackers. "And I must say you did look awfully funny!"

"Huh!" interrupts Sherman. "Not as funny as you. You couldn't even ..." But Sherman can't think what to say. Sometimes he gets very muddled. Brian looks at the two animals and says, "Stop quarrelling, both of you. *I* was the one who fell out of the tree and I don't care who knows about it. After all, everyone does silly things. Nobody is perfect."

12 January

Near the river

"I don't know about you, but I'm still hungry," says Brian. "I think I'll go fishing." "Fish taste nice," mumbles Mr Crackers, wistfully. "You scoffed the lot last time you caught a fish. Perhaps this time, you'll leave a bit for me!" Mr Crackers flies over to take his place on Brian's shoulder. The two friends feel happy again and Brian has almost forgotten a certain sheep called Sherman. But Sherman has never seen a bear fishing. He decides to join Brian and Mr Crackers on their way to the river.

13 January

All that noise

Our friends have nearly reached the river. Suddenly, they hear a loud, clucking noise. It's coming from Farmer George's farmyard. "What on earth's going on?" exclaims Sherman. "*I don't know,*" replies Mr Crackers, peevishly. But to tell you the truth, he's longing to find out what's happening. "Don't tell me, you both want to know what's going on," grumbles Brian. "You don't care about me feeling hungry!"

14 January

The Cock-a-doodle-doo family

Farmer George's farm is not very large, and the animals who live there are all his friends. There's Clara the cow, who everyone thinks must be as old as Farmer George himself. And there's Father and Mother Goose, and all their children. Farmer George has built a lovely wooden shed for his hens. But it's so beautifully built, it's more like a house than a shed. The Cock-a-doodle-doo family live there. And that's where all the noise is coming from.

15 January

Cluck, cluck, cluck

"My eggs, my eggs! Albert, you stupid cockerel, where are my eggs? I just go out for five minutes to have a chat with Mother Goose, and you can't look after them! And now they're all lost! Oh dear, my precious little chicks waiting to come out of their shells, all lost! Who could have stolen them?"

Our friends arrive on the scene at the same time as Farmer George and Mother Goose, with all her children. Everyone is wondering what could have happened.

16 January

A fox?

"Hello Brian, Hello Mr Crackers, Hi! Sherman. Nice to see you all again," says Farmer George. "Does anyone know what's going on?" "No," answers Brian. "I think Mrs Cock-a-doodle-doo has lost her eggs," suggests Sherman. "It must have been that wicked fox. He's been after my children," adds Mother Goose. Albert and Mrs Cock-a-doodle-doo come out of their house. Everyone talks at once. No one is sure what has happened.

17 January

A good idea

"My eggs have been stolen," cries Mrs Cock-a-doodle-doo. "I only laid them yesterday. That stupid cockerel couldn't even spare five minutes to look after them." Albert is standing beside her, looking very sheepish.
"It must have been that wicked fox," cries Mother Goose. She's sure he wants to eat all her children. "Calm down, all of you," orders Farmer George. "I know it's very upsetting, but Mrs Cock-a-doodle-doo can lay some more eggs. And next time, Albert, take better care of them." Everyone thinks this is a good idea. Mrs Cock-a-doodle-doo goes back indoors to lay another egg. Albert is so relieved, he starts crowing.

19

18 January

Cake

"I'm starving," says Brian. "What about going fishing?" "*You* can go fishing if you like," replies Farmer George. "But *I've* just baked a lovely cherry cake, and it's ready to come out of the oven." Brian stands and stares while Farmer George's words sink in. "Cake! Did you say cake?" he cries. Everyone laughs while Farmer George takes his cake out of the oven and puts it on the table in the garden. How delicious it looks. *All* the animals realize they're absolutely starving. Brian soon has cream all over his face. Sherman munches happily on a piece of cake, while Mr Crackers pecks at a cherry.

When the cake is finished, Brian, Mr Crackers and Sherman say goodbye to kind Farmer George and set off once again for the river.

19 January

Not full yet?

A cherry cake from Farmer George
Is perfect for a picnic.
My tummy rumbles all the time,
While I wait to eat it.

But Brian Bear can hardly wait
To gobble up his helping.
He didn't catch a fish today,
He's absolutely starving!

Terry

The three friends soon catch up with Terry the tortoise, who is ambling slowly along the path to the river. "Hello, Terry," cries Brian. "What are you doing here?" "Oh, I'm just rooting around, hoping to find a nice juicy leaf for my dinner," answers the tortoise. "Do you like wild lettuce?" asks Mr Crackers. "I saw some growing by the river." "Oh, yes! It's my favourite," says Terry, as his tongue flicks out to lick his lips with pleasure. "Well, I'm going fishing," says Brian. "Mr Crackers and Sherman are coming too. Why don't you join us?" "I'd like to," replies Terry. "But you lot never remember I've got such short legs, I can't keep up with you." "Why don't you sit on my back?" suggests Brian. "Then I can carry you down to the river." Terry thinks this a terrific idea. It's quite a struggle for the tortoise to clamber onto Brian's back, but after a while the four friends are happily making their way along the path to the river.

21 January

Splash!

At last they reach the river. "You'll find the wild lettuce over there," chirps Mr Crackers, as Terry slowly wanders off to look for his dinner. Then Sherman and Mr Crackers watch nervously as Brian stands on the very edge of the river bank. "Come and look!," cries Brian as he turns towards his friends, holding his arms out open wide. "You've never seen fish like this. They're mega!" "Watch out!" shouts Mr Crackers. But it's too late. Brian topples over the edge of the bank, and with a mighty splash, falls into the river.

22 January

I've caught a fish

Sherman and Mr Crackers are very worried that Brian might have hurt himself. Then they begin to laugh. Brian looks so funny sitting in the river. "I don't know what you're laughing at," splutters Brian crossly. This only makes the two friends laugh until their sides ache. "That was the biggest splash I've ever seen," gasps Mr Crackers. Brian wipes the water from his eyes. "I think I've caught a fish," he says calmly. "I don't believe it," says Mr Crackers. "I think I've landed on one," replies Brian proudly, as he lifts a huge fish out of the water. "So that's how bears go fishing," says Sherman, as he looks at the fish in amazement.

23 January

Sleeping

When Brian has eaten every scrap of fish, he complains of feeling sleepy. "That's because you ate so much," says Mr Crackers, "you're ever so greedy." "I always lie down and think when I've eaten a lot," baas Sherman, helpfully. "That's all very well, but *I* just need to sleep," Brian grumbles. "Have a nap, then," calls Terry from the wild lettuce patch. "It's time I sang a song," says Mr Crackers.
Brian makes himself comfortable beneath a large hollow tree. Mr Crackers flies up onto a branch and starts singing. "How can a bear sleep with all that noise?" mutters Brian, grumpily. "If you don't like my singing, I'll find another tree," says Mr Crackers crossly, as he flies away.

24 January

Brian has a dream

Brian settles down and goes to sleep. He snores gently as the sun shines warmly on his face. He's eaten so much, he soon starts dreaming about big fish, enormous cakes and all the adventures he has had with Mr Crackers. Then Brian finds himself dreaming about that scary time when he was stalked by a man out hunting. What a big gun he had! He even fired it at Brian. And what a fierce dog he had with him. Brian starts to toss and turn in his sleep. How fast he had to run! He even lost his way because he was so frightened. But Mr Crackers came to his rescue! He flew high above the trees and told him how to escape from the hunter. That was the first time they had met. And Brian's dreams become happy again as he remembers his good friend.

25 January

Snoozing song

Mr Crackers sings his song,
But Brian doesn't hear it.
He wants to snooze the whole day long,
Without his coat or blanket.
An icy breeze chills the air
But he doesn't seem to feel it!

26 January

Time passes

And so the summer passes by and soon the days grow shorter. There's frost in the air and the leaves on the trees start to change colour. Brian has been enjoying himself, eating all sorts of delicious food to get ready for the winter. Mr Crackers looks at his friend a little sadly, because he knows that bears go to sleep at this time of the year. They don't wake up until the spring; they sleep through all the winter. The thought of this makes Mr Crackers feel miserable. Without the friendly bear to keep him company, Mr Crackers feels rather lonely.

27 January

The bear's house

Brian's house is in the middle of the forest. It's really just a cave; not a very large cave, but big enough for a bear like Brian. Brian has made his home extremely comfortable. He has laid grass and leaves on the floor to make a bed. It will be warm and dry for the winter. The floor is carpeted with the softest moss underneath the bed, so Brian has made the finest bed a sleepy bear could wish for.

28 January

William Squirrel

There's an oak tree in front of Brian's house. It's so old that it has begun to turn a little hollow. But that's no problem for William Squirrel. He has been busy all summer making himself a lovely den inside. Now he's collecting acorns to build up his stores for the winter. It's very hard work because William has to run all the way down the tree trunk to collect them. Then he has to bury the acorns and remember where he's hidden them. When the ground is covered with snow, he won't see where he's put them.

29 January

A tree full of homes

William is not the only creature living in the old oak tree. It's more like an apartment block. One of William's neighbours is Mrs Woodpecker: William doesn't get on very well with her because she makes such a lot of noise building herself new houses. "When will that stupid bird stop pecking at the tree?" mutters William, as he covers his ears with his paws. "She sounds worse than a road mender!"

But today everything is peaceful. Suddenly, he spies Brian and Mr Crackers coming towards him.

"Hi there!" he calls. "What are you two doing?"

Brian looks so sleepy, he can hardly keep his eyes open.

"I'm turning in for my long winter sleep," replies Brian.

"Sleep well, my friend," says Mr Crackers as he watches Brian disappear inside his house. "I'll see you in the spring."

30 January

Snow

Brian wakes up, slowly opens his eyes and looks around his den. He's had a lovely long sleep in his comfy bed of grass and leaves. Can it be spring already? "Perhaps it's turned warmer outside at last, and I can go out to find some food," thinks Brian as he rolls over and stretches. "All that sleep has made me feel hungry." Brian gives himself a good scratch and then walks over to the entrance of his cave. "Everything looks so strange," he says, as he peers out of the doorway. It's a white world outside and Brian thinks he's dreaming. "I'll wake up soon and there'll be butterflies flying around my nose," says Brian as he smiles to himself. Butterflies always fly around a bear's nose, especially when he falls asleep among the flowers. Brian shuts his eyes tightly and then opens them again. The world is still white! What's happening?

31 January

A white world

Brian stands in the snow, with a surprised expression on his face as he looks around him. "This is *very* odd," says Brian, scratching his head. "It wasn't like this when I went to sleep." Poor Brian is almost frightened. He's never seen anything like this before. Large white flakes of snow are falling onto his head. One even lands on his nose. "Atishoo, Atishoo-oo!" he sneezes. "Don't catch cold standing there," warns a friendly voice. Brian looks around and sees Mr Crackers. "Hello, there," calls Brian in relief. He's ever so glad to see his friend. "What's all this cold white stuff?" he asks. "It's called snow," chirps Mr Crackers as he flies down to perch on Brian's shoulder. "I'm very sorry, Brian. The winter isn't over yet, you've woken up too early!"

1 February

One step at a time

Brian carefully places one foot in front of the other. They both disappear under the thick layer of snow. "Oh no, my feet have disappeared!" he grumbles. Then he tries again. "My goodness," he yells. "My feet are freezing!" Mr Crackers can hardly stop himself laughing. "It's a good thing you're so fat," he giggles. "And you've got a warm fur coat, so why are you complaining?" "Because I'm starving!" growls Brian. "Let's see if we can find anything to eat," suggests Mr Crackers, soothingly.

2 February

Lifting your feet

Brian plods bearfully through the snow. "You must lift your feet up, otherwise you'll trip over something," warns Mr Crackers. He has hardly got the words out of his mouth before Brian falls flat on his face in the snow. "What did you say?" asks Brian plaintively. Poor Brian! He's tripped over a branch, hidden in the snow. There's snow in his eyes, snow in his mouth. There's even snow up his nose! "You must walk carefully," Mr Crackers tries to explain, but Brian has already discovered this the hard way!

3 February

A light

Brian and Mr Crackers have been walking for quite a long time before they suddenly see a small light, flickering in the distance. "What's that?" asks Brian. "I didn't know anyone lived in this part of the forest." Everything looks so different in the snow, the two friends have lost their sense of direction. "Let's go and see where the light's coming from," suggests Brian. "That's a good idea," agrees Mr Crackers as he flies on to lead the way ahead.

4 February

Cosy and warm

The light is coming from a small cottage at the edge of the forest. Brian and Mr Crackers peep through a little window. Inside, it looks so warm and cosy. A fire is burning in the grate, and the two friends can see steam rising invitingly from the pot that is hanging over it. Someone is moving in the room, and Brian has to peer through the frost on the window pane to catch a glimpse of the owner. A little old woman passes the window and comes to open the door.
"It looks as though I have more guests today," she says cheerfully.

5 February

Soup

"Do come in, my friends, it's lovely and warm inside." Brian and Mr Crackers stand there looking rather shy. "We don't want to disturb you, but we saw a light shining from the window." The two friends are shivering while they stand on the doorstep. "Do come in, won't you," the old lady says. "My poor old bones will get a chill if I stand here any longer. Besides the soup is just about ready." Soup! Brian just can't resist soup. "Thank you," says Brian gratefully, as he leads the way. His stomach is beginning to rumble.

6 February

Miss Peggy

"I'm called Brian, and this is my friend Mr Crackers," says Brian, politely. "My name is Miss Peggy," replies the old lady. "Go and sit by the fire and you'll soon get warm." Brian stares around the room. It's really cosy. There are lots of pots and bottles on the shelves, as well as bunches of herbs hanging from the ceiling. Brian has never seen anything like it! But it's lovely and warm and Miss Peggy is so friendly. "Why have you never come to visit me before?" asks Miss Peggy. "We didn't know you lived here," explains Brian shyly.

7 February

A talking snowman

Brian pushes his way through the bunches of herbs to reach the fireside. He suddenly notices a large white figure sitting in a chair, squashed into a corner. Who could this be, he wonders. A snowman in the cottage? But that's impossible! "Ahem," says the snowman. Brian is rather frightened. What's this, a talking snowman? Then the large white figure gets to its feet and Brian sees that it's an enormous bear! "Pleased to meet you, I'm sure. I'm a polar bear and my name is Icicle."

8 February

Icicle's story

Miss Peggy gives them all a bowl of tasty soup. "Oh, it's delicious," exclaims Brian. "I didn't know how hungry I was!" he sighs happily. When they have all finished, Icicle begins to tell his story. "I come from the North Pole," he says. "It sometimes snows so hard, you can't see one paw in front of the other." Brian looks at him in astonishment. "Don't you go to sleep in the winter?" he asks. "Where I come from, it's always winter," Icicle explains. "How would I know when to sleep and when to wake up? No, I sleep whenever I'm tired. I snuggle up in my den and stay there as long as I can."

9 February

Beauty

"But I take a holiday once a year," Icicle continues. "Then I make for warmer places, like your forest here." "I wouldn't call it *that* warm," interrupts Mr Crackers. "It seems freezing cold to me." Icicle looks down his nose at cheeky Mr Crackers. "You've never been to the North Pole," says the frosty polar bear. Beauty, Miss Peggy's cat, has been sitting quietly, listening to Icicle's story. Suddenly, she starts to shiver. All this talk of snow and ice is making her feel chilly. She jumps onto Miss Peggy's lap. "That's much more comfortable," purrs Beauty.

10 February

Far from home

Everything is still and white,
Even at the dead of night,
In Icicle's land of snow.
The polar bear decides to go
Far away from ice and snow.
He leaves his land of cold behind
To see what new things he can find
Floating on an ice floe.

11 February

Early to bed

Beauty is purring contentedly on Miss Peggy's lap. "More soup for anyone?" asks Miss Peggy. "You should never ask bears a question like that. They always want second helpings!" laughs Mr Crackers. "That doesn't matter, there's plenty more for everyone," replies Miss Peggy. "I think we should all go to bed early, because we can have lots of fun in the snow tomorrow," twinkles Miss Peggy, with little stars in her eyes. No sooner said than done. Warmed by the soup, everyone looks for somewhere to sleep. Before very long, Miss Peggy's house is full of the sound of gentle snoring.

A little careful?

"Let's go out and enjoy the snow," says Miss Peggy with a mischievous smile. "Aren't you a bit old for that kind of thing?" asks Mr Crackers, his voice showing his surprise. "Of course not," replies Miss Peggy. "I'm still ace at throwing snowballs. But I've never been tobogganing. I'm longing to have a go!" Mr Crackers is not at all sure about Miss Peggy going tobogganing. "She ought to be more careful at her age," he grumbles. Miss Peggy puts on her bobble-hat, her thickest sweater, and a long woollen scarf. Now she's ready for anything!

13 February

A day of fun

What fun they have in the snow! Miss Peggy builds a magnificent snowman which looks rather like a bear. Then they all have a snowball fight. Miss Peggy's aim is so good, Beauty runs away and hides. Mr Crackers almost gets hit on the beak by one of her snowballs. And Icicle is not fast enough to dodge one aimed at his ear! "Yippee!" yells Miss Peggy as her snowballs find their mark. "Too old for snowball fights, you say!" She has a wonderful time. "I feel quite young again," she cries with glee. When everyone is sitting back at the fireside again, feeling glowing, Miss Peggy says: "Now it's time for a story."

14 February

The North Pole

Icicle starts to tell them about the North Pole. About how cold it is there, and about all that snow. But most of all, he tells them about his friends. There's Wally the walrus who is so good at fishing. Wally likes drifting on an ice floe until it almost melts. Then he plunges into the sea and goes for a swim with his great friend, Eric the whale. "Are they cousins?" asks Brian. Icicle looks puzzled. "What makes you think that?" he asks. "Well," says Brian, "the words walrus and whale are so alike, they could be related." Everyone laughs because no-one could call Brian a brainy bear.

15 February

Inuits

"Who else lives at the North Pole?" asks Mr Crackers. "Well, there are the Arctic wolves and the Arctic hares. But it's hard to spot them because their fur is as white as the snow," Icicle tells them. "And reindeer, of course. They run so fast, it looks as though they are flying over the snow!" "Do any humans live near the North Pole?" asks Brian. "Yes, of course, a few people do," replies Icicle. "They're called Inuits. They live in special houses called igloos and they go hunting. Igloos are made of ice and snow." Brian and Mr Crackers can hardly believe their ears. How can anyone live in a house made from ice? It must be freezing cold! Icicle shakes his head. "They're lovely and warm inside," he tells them. It's quite late now. "Time for bed, everyone," says Miss Peggy. "Icicle has a long journey ahead of him tomorrow."

16 February

Icicle sets off

Miss Peggy gets up early the next morning. "Wake up, everybody," she says. "Icicle has a long journey." Brian wipes the sleep out of his eyes. "Mmmm, what's that lovely smell?" Miss Peggy has cooked a lovely breakfast, and there's even a jar of honey on the table! Mr Crackers is sitting at the breakfast table, nibbling some seed cake. "I'm afraid I've already started," he apologizes, as the others take their seats. When they have finished breakfast, it's time for Icicle to set off on his journey. He packs his things into a little suitcase. "Goodbye, everybody," he says, "See you all next year!" Miss Peggy, Beauty, Brian, and Mr Crackers wave him on his way. They're sad to see the walking 'snowman' leave them.

17 February

Chopping wood

"Is there anything I can do to help you, Miss Peggy?" Brian asks. "You could chop some wood for the fire," she replies. "It's nearly all used up, and you *do* have big strong muscles." Brian smiles with pride and sets to work. There's a pile of logs and a chopping block outside the house, and each time Brian brings down the axe onto a log, splinters fly. Mr Crackers is watching from a safe distance, giving advice. "That's done," grunts Brian at last. "There's plenty of firewood ready now." And he stacks it beside Miss Peggy's house.

18 February

Toothache

Brian and Mr Crackers go into the house. "Did you manage to chop all that wood?" asks Miss Peggy. "Of course we did," says Mr Crackers, proudly. "But now we're rather tired." Brian looks at Mr Crackers crossly. "All *you* did was sit on a branch giving advice! Did *that* make you tired?" Miss Peggy can't help laughing at them both. Then she suddenly notices that Brian's cheek looks red and swollen. "I think I'm starting toothache," says Brian gloomily. "I'll put a cloth round your head to keep you warm," says Miss Peggy gently, as she ties a large towel round Brian's head. "That should make you better."

41

19 February

Brian is in a bad mood

Brian has been in a bad mood all afternoon. "You eat too many sweet things," says Mr Crackers. "That's why you've got toothache." Brian feels grumpier than ever. "Oh, shut your beak," growls Brian. "You haven't even got any teeth, so what do you know about it?" Mr Crackers feels sorry for his friend. "People used to tie a piece of string to the sore tooth, then tie the other end to a door handle," says Mr Crackers. "Then they waited for someone to come into the room and open the door. It should pull out the tooth, but it's *very* dangerous." Brian is prepared to risk it. Soon, he has the string set up, and he's sitting nervously, waiting for Miss Peggy to come home.

20 February

Ouch!

Mr Crackers sits at the window, watching out for Miss Peggy's return. "How much longer do I have to sit here waiting?" grumbles Brian. The string is stretched across the room, swinging from side to side as he speaks. Suddenly, Mr Crackers sees Miss Peggy walking briskly up the garden path, but he doesn't tell Brian. Miss Peggy opens the door, and with a sudden jerk Brian's sore tooth jumps out of his mouth. "Ouch!" cries Brian. Miss Peggy stands and looks at him in surprise. "What on earth are you doing?" she asks. "*We* didn't do anything, but *you* have just pulled out Brian's tooth," explains Mr Crackers. "And now it's gone, it won't give me any more trouble," says Brian.

21 February

Moving

"Have you noticed that spring is coming?" asks Miss Peggy, when she has got over the shock of Brian's cry of pain. "The snow is beginning to melt and I saw the first snowdrops this morning. It won't be long now before I can move house." Brian and Mr Crackers look at Miss Peggy in horror. "Move? Why do you want to move? It's so nice here. We love staying with you," they both cry out at once. Miss Peggy begins to laugh. "I know this sounds weird, but my house can fly. It's frozen to the ground in winter, but when the spring comes, it can fly again."

22 February

Confused

Brian doesn't know what to say, he's dumb with amazement. He looks at Mr Crackers, and wonders if Miss Peggy is a little touched in the head, or if this is for real. Perhaps she really *is* mad, she's such an old lady. Miss Peggy looks at the two friends and sees their worried expressions. "Let's all have a glass of lemonade, and then I'll explain," she says. Now Brian is quite certain. Miss Peggy must have fallen over and had a nasty bump on her head. That's the only explanation.

23 February

Miss Peggy's magic

Brian and Mr Crackers sit and listen with open mouths to everything Miss Peggy tells them. "Wizard Gombal gave me this little house because I am one of his best pupils," Miss Peggy explains. "He also knows I'm so *very* fond of travelling." Brian looks at Miss Peggy in awe. "Are you really a wizard's pupil? Can you perform magic?" he asks. Miss Peggy looks a little crestfallen. "I'm not as good as Wizard Gombal, but my magic works quite well sometimes." Brian almost chokes on his lemonade and shakes his head. Who ever would have believed it?

24 February

Not a witch

"Isn't that a bit nasty ... I mean ... Doing magic and things like that?" asks Brian, nervously. "Doesn't it always end in tears?" Miss Peggy begins to laugh. "Oh no, I'm not a *wicked* witch, I just try to help everyone." That makes Brian feel much better, because he's very fond of Miss Peggy. That evening he sits alone in the corner, imagining all the adventures they could have with a house that flies. He stares into space, it's all so confusing.

25 February

A little elf

The next day, Brian gets up at the crack of dawn. Everyone else is still asleep, it's that early. The sun is shining, and the snow has almost gone. Here and there, a few white patches of melting snow remain among the trees. Brian is careful to step over them. A brisk walk in the early morning is just the thing for a bear. What a strange tale Brian had heard the night before, he can still hardly believe it. Miss Peggy has a *flying* house. And she has the gift of magic! Brian's head starts to spin when he tries to remember everything Miss Peggy told him. Suddenly he hears a mysterious noise coming from the bushes. He goes over to see what it is, out of curiosity. As he draws near, he hears a little voice crying out, "Please help me." When Brian looks more closely, he sees a little elf, sobbing in a bramble bush.

26 February

Helpless

"Who are you?" asks Brian in surprise. "Aren't you going to help me first?" cries the little elf. "I'm freezing cold and my wings are caught on these thorns." Brian lifts some of the briars away and sees the problem. The little elf is trapped on the brambles. "How tiny he is," thinks Brian, in wonder. "Can't you do something to help?" cries the little elf. Brian comes out of his dream, and he releases the elf's wings from the thorns as delicately as any bear could. "Thank you," says the elf, as he shakes out his wings and looks at them. "Oh no! How can I fly with torn wings?" asks the elf desperately.

27 February

Mustardseed

Brian feels very sorry for the little elf. "Can I do anything to help?" he asks kindly. "Can you mend my wings for me?" the elf asks doubtfully. "No, but I think I know someone who can," says Brian. Hadn't Miss Peggy told him she had the gift of magic? The elf looks at Brian hopefully. "Who can mend my wings?" he asks. "Miss Peggy!" says Brian, triumphantly. "Hooray," cries the elf. "I was just on my way to see her. Can you take me to Miss Peggy's cottage?" "That won't be very difficult," says Brian with a smile. "I just happen to be staying with her." The little elf looks at Brian gratefully. "I'm so glad you came along. My name is Mustardseed. What's yours?" "I'm Brian," the bear answers shyly.

28 February

So little

Brian picks up Mustardseed in his great bear paws. "How tiny you are," he says. "And you weigh almost nothing." "Elves are never very large," says Mustardseed. "Your fur is so warm," he adds, "I feel better already." Brian smiles happily. "We must go and find Miss Peggy at once," he says. "Well I never!" cries Miss Peggy when Brian and Mustardseed arrive back at her cottage. "My poor little friend! Whatever happened to you?" "I was on my way to visit you when I suddenly felt icy cold, then I fell into a thorn bush." "Have a little rest first, and then I'll try to mend your wings for you," comforts Miss Peggy.

29 February

Help needed

Miss Peggy takes down some pots from her shelves and brews a magic poultice for Mustardseed's wings. When the elf starts to feel better, Miss Peggy says: "Now, tell me why you were coming to see me." "They need your help in the great Misty Forest. Such strange things are happening," Mustardseed replies. "The animals are disappearing. The last one to vanish was the frog princess, and we just don't know what's happened to her." Miss Peggy looks thoughtful. Then her expression changes. "Oh, that's bound to be the work of a wicked witch called Endora. I think it's high time my little cottage prepared itself to fly again, then we can set off in the morning. Brian, will you and Mr Crackers come with me? We could do with your help." "Of course," replies Brian, looking at Mr Crackers. "We wouldn't miss this for anything!"

47

1 March

Flying

Little house, rise up and fly,
Fly with the wind into the sky,
Sail along above the trees,
Above the houses, into the breeze,
All the way to the Misty Forest.
Swiftly through the clouds we sail,
Safe from every storm and gale
'Til we come to rest in the forest.

2 March

The search

Brian really enjoys the flight. He looks down from the upstairs window of the cottage in amazement. He's so surprised to see how different everything looks from the air. "There's Farmer George's house," he cries. "How small it seems." Soon they are flying over villages, hills, and valleys that Brian has never seen before. They've left his forest far behind them. How enormous the world is, thinks Brian. They draw near to the Misty Forest as evening falls. Miss Peggy spots a good landing place and brings her cottage gently back to earth. "We can stay here for a day or two Mustardseed, until your wings are quite mended," she says. "Tomorrow, Brian and Mr Crackers can go hunting in the Misty Forest. Would you like that?" They certainly would. What an adventure! "But first you must go and see Joseph Owl. He'll be able to give you directions," says Mustardseed.

3 March

Joseph

"It feels rather frightening here," whispers Brian to Mr Crackers. His friend is sitting in his usual place on Brian's shoulder. "I think we're on the outskirts of the Misty Forest," replies Mr Crackers, with a shiver. "I do hope Joseph is at home," murmurs Brian. "I'm feeling rather tired and gloomy." "I expect he's at home having a snooze," says Mr Crackers encouragingly. "Look, there he is! Hello, Joseph. Wake up, you've got visitors!"

4 March

Too-whit-too-woo

"Too-whit-too-woo – what's the matter? Is there a fire?" cries
Joseph as he wakes up with a start. "No, you have some
visitors. This is my friend Brian. My name's Mr Crackers."
"Whooo – why did you wake me up?" asks Joseph, sleepily.
"We heard the frog princess has disappeared. We thought you
might know something about it," says Brian. "Yes, I do,"
replies Joseph. "I saw that wicked witch Endora magic her
away. And now the frog king is broken-hearted."

51

5 March

A witch called Endora

Everything is unnaturally quiet near the house of the wicked witch who lives in the Misty Forest, the witch called Endora. Not an animal moves, not a bird sings, not a leaf rustles. Endora is a really *wicked* witch. Her mother was a witch and so was her grandmother. One day, Endora's mother made a mistake; she accidentally cast the wrong spell and disappeared completely. Now Endora has inherited all their magic spells. She lives alone with her cat in the family house. No living creature dares come near her.

6 March

Bobby

The only friend Endora has is her cat called Bobby. And it's not surprising that Bobby is her friend. He's just as bad as his mistress. He has killed all the birds that used to live near their house. That's one of the reasons why it's so quiet in that part of the forest. All you can hear is the wind howling in the trees. But Bobby doesn't mind. He can hear if anyone comes. And Endora doesn't miss the birds either, because she's rather deaf and hates birds anyway.

7 March

Magic potion

Endora is standing by her fire, stirring a huge cauldron. "Hubble, bubble, rubble, stubble. If you cross me, there'll be trouble," she chants to herself. "Miaow," purrs Bobby, pressing his head against her leg. "Don't disturb me, Bobby, I'm busy. You'll confuse me and I'll end up magicking myself away, just like my dear mother." Bobby stalks across to the window seat. "Don't get in the way when your mistress is busy," snarls Bobby, mimicking his mistress. "But I feel like doing something bad, like catching a bird, or digging my claws into a small furry animal."

8 March

Horatio

It is unnaturally quiet around Endora's house. But that doesn't mean *all* the animals have left the great Misty Forest. There's still Horatio Hogge, for instance. Actually, Horatio is an ordinary pig, but he decided to change his surname to Hogge because he thought it made his name sound grander. "What's more, it makes the other animals treat me with more respect. And that can't be bad," says Horatio.

9 March

Nico's castle

Nico Badger lives all alone in a little house, close to the path by the three great oak trees. Nico has built himself a lovely home. You would think it was just an ordinary house from a distance. But as you draw closer, it looks more like a miniature castle. Nico is terribly proud of his home. Sometimes, he spends hours sitting with his back against one of the oak trees, admiring his work. "What a beautiful house I've built," he congratulates himself. "It's just like a little castle."

10 March

Rustle, rustle

One morning, Nico is sitting admiring his house as usual. Suddenly his daydreams are disturbed by a strange, rustling noise from the bushes. Nico looks round. "What's that? Is anyone there?" he calls sharply. Rustle, rustle, rustle. There's that noise again. "Is anyone there?" calls Nico, even more sharply. Rustle, rustle, rustle. Nico isn't frightened, because badgers are fearless creatures. Then an unnatural stillness falls on the path by the three oak trees. Nico suspects that Endora is casting her spells. He knows he must be careful because even Nico is frightened by Endora's magic.

While Nico is sitting admiring his house, Brian and Mr Crackers are making their way along the Misty Path. "It's rather foggy here, isn't it?" murmurs Brian. "Speak up, Brian, I can't hear you!" says Mr Crackers. "It's *rather* spooky here, isn't it?" murmurs Brian. "And I can't find my way in this fog." Mr Crackers looks at his friend. "You're not frightened, are you?" he asks. "What, frightened, of course not! Bears are never scared," Mr Crackers can't help smiling to himself. "Well," Brian admits at last. "It's *very* spooky here, isn't it?"

12 March

Bertie

Meanwhile, an animal is hard at work in another part of the great Misty Forest. His name is Bertie Beaver. Bertie lives by the great lake. It's a long way from Endora's house, so he isn't too bothered by her magic. Sometimes, Endora flies over the lake on her broomstick. But that doesn't give Bertie any problems, just as long as she keeps away from Beaver Lodge. Not long ago, Endora forgot one of her spells and fell into the lake with a mighty splash! How all the animals laughed, especially the frogs. Endora became very angry indeed with the frog king, because he croaked the loudest. She cast a spell on the frog princess to punish her father. The frog princess has never been seen again. Now you can understand why the frog king is broken-hearted.

13 March

Mr Fieldmouse

"I'm going to sit down now," says Brian, "and have a nice little rest." Mr Crackers thinks it's a great idea and points to a fallen tree trunk. "Lean your back against that tree and give it a good scratch," says Mr Crackers. He knows just how often a bear needs to scratch his back to stay good-tempered. Brian heaves himself onto the ground and is just about to give his back an agreeable rub when he hears an angry little voice shouting from the pathway. "What's that freak doing, blocking my front door?" Brian looks around in surprise. "You're sitting right in front of my house, you stupid bear," cries Mr Fieldmouse, shaking his fist at Brian. "You nearly flattened me, you great fat monster!" "I'm *not* fat, I'm chubby," replies Brian huffily. He feels rather offended.

14 March

An earthquake?

Brian bends down to see what all the fuss is about. Then he spots the entrance to the house. It's cleverly disguised by ferns and grass. Mr Fieldmouse rushes up to inspect his doorway. "I don't think it's damaged," he says. Then the door suddenly swings open and there stands Mrs Fieldmouse. "Oh my goodness, what was that? I thought it was an earthquake. I was afraid the whole house would collapse!" Mr Fieldmouse gives his wife a hug. "No, it was just this stupid bear not looking where he was putting his fat bottom. But don't worry, I've got rid of him," says Mr. Fieldmouse. "I am *not* fat, just a little chubby," says Brian rather crossly. "Calm down everybody, no damage has been done," says Mr Crackers. "There you are, I can't be *that* fat," says Brian.

15 March

Mouse cake

Soon everything is peaceful again at the Fieldmouse house. Brian has said he's sorry to have caused so much bother and is sitting down quietly, having his rest. To tell you the truth, he's feeling rather embarrassed. But he soon cheers up when Mrs Fieldmouse comes out of the house with a freshly baked mouse cake which she offers to Brian. He looks at the tiny cake in his paw. "I could eat ten of those," he thinks. "Is this a hint I should go on a diet?" But, of course, he doesn't say anything. "Enjoy your cake, Brian," says Mr Crackers as he notices his friend's expression. "Mmmm, it's delicious," replies Brian as he swallows it whole. "We never expected anyone with such a large appetite," apologizes Mrs Fieldmouse. "At least I won't put on any weight," jokes Brian, and everyone laughs.

16 March

From far away

Mrs Fieldmouse can't stop herself from being nosy any longer. "Where do you come from?" she asks. "What are you doing here? We're not used to bears in the Misty Forest." "We've come from far away," replies Brian. Then he tells Mr and Mrs Fieldmouse about Miss Peggy and Mustardseed, the little elf. "And so," he says, as he finishes his story, "we're on our way to visit the frog king. Joseph Owl gave us directions, but I think we've lost our way. It's so foggy here in the forest."

17 March

The wrong path

"You've taken the wrong path," says Mr Fieldmouse. "Look, keep going straight on until you come to the hare path. Follow the hare path until you come to the three oak trees. That's where Nico Badger lives. Ask him for more directions." "But mind you don't sit on *his* roof by mistake," interrupts Mrs Fieldmouse. "You won't live to see another day. Badgers are ever so fierce!" Brian promises to be more careful next time he sits down, and waves a cheerful goodbye to the fieldmice.·

18 March

The hare path

Jumping here, jumping there,
Hares are jumping everywhere.
Some jump over, some twirl round,
Some are rolling on the ground.
Through their tunnels they go chasing,
Hiding, seeking, springing, racing.
What a lot of hares we see,
When we watch them carefully.

19 March

Nowhere to be seen

At last, Brian and Mr Crackers reach the three oak trees, but they can't find Nico.
Apart from a few hares playing hide and seek, there doesn't seem to
be anyone around. "Would you mind flying up to that branch,
Mr Crackers?" suggests Brian. "You might spot Nico's house."
Mr Crackers flies up to the branch and looks to the left and right,
but he can't see anything. "I'll just fly over there," he decides.
You've guessed what happens next! Mr Crackers is perching on Nico's roof.
"Come over here! I think I've found Nico's house," he shouts at Brian.

20 March

Angry

Nico rushes out of his house and looks around
angrily. "What's that noise?" he cries in a terrible
voice. "Who's disturbed my midday nap? Come here
you rascal!" Oh dear, winces Brian. Now we've upset
Nico Badger. This isn't a good start to our adventure.
"I'm very sorry to inconvenience you," he apologizes
to Nico. "We were sent here by the fieldmice. They
think you may be able to help us." Brian tells his
story, and Nico calms down slowly. "Ah, now I
understand," says Nico, and he gives Brian and Mr
Crackers new directions. "Good luck," cries Nico
as he disappears back into his house.
"Don't wake me up again!"

21 March

Getting late

On their way to the lake, Brian and Mr Crackers pause from time to time to eat some berries. But they don't waste *too* much time because they want to arrive at the lake before nightfall. It's already late afternoon when Mr Crackers flies on ahead. "We've nearly reached the lake," he reports back to Brian. "If you keep going straight on, you'll come to Beaver Lodge. I've already warned Bertie you're on your way. He'll take us to the frog king." It's dark when Brian finally reaches Beaver Lodge. "I think it would be better to see the king in the morning," says Bertie. Brian has fallen asleep before Bertie has finished speaking. He's so tired from all his walking.

22 March

The frogs

The next morning, Brian and Mr Crackers start the day with a huge breakfast. Lots of berries grow beside the lake, and they have so many to choose from. "Now I feel strong enough for anything," declares Brian. "Will you show us the way to the frog king, Bertie?" The three friends walk beside the lake until they come to the place where bulrushes grow. "This is where the frogs live," says Bertie. "Wait a moment, I'll just let them know you're here." And he disappears among the reeds. After a short while, he returns and invites our friends to follow him.

23 March

What a noise

Suddenly, Brian and Mr Crackers find themselves surrounded by hundreds of excited frogs. Croak, croak, croak! What a noise they make, Brian is almost deafened. "Silence," croaks the largest frog. He is the frog king. Before long, everyone is quiet and they are able to talk. "Welcome, my friends. I must apologize for all this noise," croaks the frog king. "My people were so excited when Bertie told us that you have come to rescue my daughter. They all love her so much. The frog queen has been sick with grief since she disappeared. I, too, am very sad at losing my daughter. I long to have her safely home."

24 March

Very flattered

Brian is rather alarmed when he hears what the frog king has to say. Rescue the princess? He hadn't thought of that. Miss Peggy only sent him to search for her. This sounds much more dangerous. The frogs are silent as they look hopefully at Brian. When he sees the deeply saddened eyes of the king, Brian cannot bear the thought of disappointing him. In fact, he feels very flattered that this noble frog has so much confidence in him. He takes a deep breath. "I will bring your princess safely home," says Brian.

25 March

Mad with excitement

All at once, the frogs burst out into a deafening roar. They are mad with excitement now. They had noticed Brian was rather unwilling to help them. They were afraid Bertie had made a mistake about the bear. But now Brian has promised to bring their princess home. Oh, how happy they are again. Brian, Mr Crackers, and Bertie press their hands to their ears to protect themselves from the noise of the frogs' happy voices. Mr Crackers looks across at Brian. "This is a fine mess you've got us into," he mutters. At last, the noise dies down. "How will you bring my daughter home?" the king asks Brian. Everyone listens attentively, waiting to hear Brian's plan.

You never know

Brian's jaw drops and his mouth hangs open. "I ... er ... We ... er," he stammers. Then he has a brilliant idea for a bear. "I can't tell you what I plan to do, because you never know who might be listening." All the frogs nod their heads. "You never know who you can trust," they croak in agreement. Brian is ever so pleased with himself. He has managed to get out of a sticky situation. After the frog king has thanked the two friends once again, the frogs watch Brian and Mr Crackers set out to find that wicked witch Endora. "Nice creatures, those frogs. But they do croak a lot," remarks Brian to Mr Crackers.

27 March

Someone knows

Endora has not been idle. She has always known that Brian and Mr Crackers have come to the forest. How did she find out? That's one of her many secrets. She even knows they plan to rescue the frog princess. But Endora isn't worried. In fact, she thinks it's a good joke. What fun she'll have using her magic spells to play nasty tricks! "Bobby," she cackles. "Those animals are in for a big surprise. I won't disappoint them!" Endora picks up her book of magic spells. "Bears, bears ... yes, here we are," she murmurs. "This should work nicely." Bobby sits purring on the window seat as Endora sets to work. "I've got my eye on you, Mr Crackers," threatens Bobby.

28 March

Moving house again

Horatio Hogge is sitting in the sun,
wallowing in a pool of mud.
Mmmm, this is lovely, he thinks to
himself. Mud, beautiful mud!
"Hello, Horatio," says Endora from
behind his back. Horatio jumps
out of his skin. "Oh no, not that
horrid witch again," he mutters.
"I never hear her coming." He turns
to face Endora. "Have you seen a
fat bear with a bird on his shoulder?"
asks the witch sternly. Horatio looks
into her eyes and begins to stammer.
"Er ... er ... no," he replies in a nervous
voice. I'm getting out of here as
soon as I can, vows Horatio. I've
had enough of Endora's magic!

65

29 March

The motorized broomstick

Endora is so thrilled by the idea of playing nasty tricks on Brian and Mr Crackers, she sets out on her broomstick to look for them. "I need to do something about this broomstick," she declares. "It will hardly last another winter. What I really need is a *motorized* broomstick, but where will I find one?" Suddenly Endora has an idea. She quickly flies back to her house, and gets out her vacuum cleaner. After mumbling a few magic words, Endora is happy. Now she has her motorized broomstick. The animals look up in alarm when they hear the witch coming. Then they feel slightly relieved. Endora does not realize that her new broomstick is very noisy. In future, when Endora is out and about, the animals will have a few moments warning.

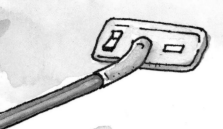

30 March

Back to Miss Peggy?

Brian and Mr Crackers spot Endora flying around. How they laugh when they see her new broomstick. "I wouldn't laugh so much if I were you," grumbles Horatio, when he spies the two friends coming towards him. "Why ever not?" asks Brian. "Endora's just been round to find out whether I've seen a bird and a bear together, and I don't think she was being friendly!" grunts Horatio. Mr Crackers looks at Brian in alarm. "Then she already knows we're here," he gulps nervously. "I think we ought to go back to Miss Peggy. She'll know what to do next." Brian feels the same as Mr Crackers, but he doesn't want to give up so easily. "We're so close to Endora's house, we might as well take a look," says Brian bravely.

31 March

Dead quiet

Everything is unnaturally quiet around Endora's house. Bobby hides behind a tree as soon as he sees Brian and Mr Crackers. The sound of Endora's flying vacuum cleaner can be heard, spluttering in the distance. Then everything becomes completely still. Brian and Mr Crackers dare not even whisper to one another. Using sign language, Mr Crackers tells Brian they must slip away as quickly as possible. But Brian is no longer paying any attention to Mr Crackers. His nose is bewitched by a delicious smell. What can it be? Is it the smell of honey? Mr Crackers recognizes the look in Brian's eyes. He tries to attract his attention. But it's too late. Brian is running towards Endora's house, led by his nose to the honey.

1 April

A dull thud

Nervously, Mr Crackers flutters along the window sill.
This looks bad, he thinks to himself. Everything is
going wrong. Endora could return at any moment.
Then who knows what would happen? Why is that
stupid bear such an idiot when there's honey about?
Brian has entered the witch's kitchen. "I knew it," he
exclaims. "My nose is never mistaken!" There on the
table stands a full pot of honey. He hears Mr Crackers
shouting "No!" through the window, but his paw is
already in the honey pot. He scoops out a pawful of
honey. Mmmm ... how delicious it tastes! Brian gobbles
the honey with a smile on his face. Then he starts to feel
dizzy and sick. Everything turns black before his eyes,
and he falls to the floor with a colossal thump.

2 April

All is lost

Oh, what a stupid thing to do,
To eat the witch's honey.
She prepared it specially,
Now Brian's got a runny tummy.

Brian's such a greedy bear,
He's caught in the witch's trap.
Gotcha! the wicked Endora cries,
while Brian takes a nap!

3 April

Just in time

Mr Crackers has seen it all through the window. He stares at Brian lying motionless on the floor. "Oh, what a stupid bear you are," he mutters to himself. "I warned you not to go inside the house. Now look what's happened!" Mr Crackers stares around in alarm. He's really feeling scared. "What can I do now?" he wails. "I wish Miss Peggy were here. She would know how to save that gormless, hairy bear!" Suddenly he sees a movement out of the corner of his eye. Bobby has seized his chance and springs up to catch Mr Crackers. But Mr Crackers is too quick for Bobby. "Phew, just in the nick of time," he cries, as he escapes Bobby's sharp claws and flies off to safety.

4 April

A large cage

Mr Crackers sits and watches Endora's house from a safe distance. He doesn't have long to wait. Soon he hears Endora's broomstick as she circles round the house and makes a bumpy landing. "What a rotten pilot she is," thinks Mr Crackers. Endora strides into her house. Her cackles of laughter send shivers down Mr Crackers' spine. "What *is* she doing?" he trembles. A few minutes later, Mr Crackers sees Endora pushing a large cage out into the garden. Her evil laugh frightens Mr Crackers. Then he sees Brian in the cage. Endora is prodding him awake with her magic wand. "Who are you? mumbles Brian as he stares into Endora's sneering face. "Where am I? What's happened?"

5 April

To bed without your supper

How uncomfortable it is squashed inside the cage. "I'm afraid it's the biggest cage I've got," chuckles Endora. "It wasn't designed for such a fat bear," she sneers. "But tell me, where's your little friend?" And she gives Brian a nasty prod with her wand. Brian is very cross. "I don't know. And even if I did, I wouldn't tell you," he replies angrily. "Never mind, I'll find him before long," jeers Endora. Bobby rubs his head against her leg, but the witch looks at her cat furiously. "As for you, you blockhead, you let that bird escape. You can go to bed without your supper!" Bobby stalks off into the house and sulks on the window seat.

6 April

Ready to pounce

Mr Crackers doesn't know what to do. Miss Peggy must be warned, of course, but he can't leave poor Brian. Through the window, Mr Crackers can see Endora busy with her vacuum cleaner. He takes his chance. Quickly, he flies over to Brian and sits on top of the cage. "Where've you been all this time?" asks Brian. "Shhhh, not so loud! She'll hear us," whispers Mr Crackers, as he fiddles with the padlock. "I've already tried that," groans Brian. The two friends are so upset, they fail to notice Bobby creeping patiently towards them. Slowly, oh so slowly, he places one paw in front of the other as he approaches the cage. He draws himself together and gets ready to pounce, when …

7 April

A mighty thump

Mr Crackers suddenly becomes numb with fright. He can feel razor sharp claws piercing through his feathers. And when he sees Bobby's pitiless eyes, he thinks his last hour has come. "Let my friend go, you brute!" shouts Brian, as he shakes the bars of his cage. Brian doesn't know his own strength, he's so angry. He pushes and pulls so fiercely at the bars that the cage abruptly gives way. He's free! "Let him go, you rotten beast!" growls Brian as he swipes at Bobby, giving the cat a mighty whack with his great bear's paw.

8 April

To 'nowhere' land

"What's going on out there?" calls Endora. "I think I'd better go and have a look. And I'll take my wand with me." Endora looks round in horror. The shattered pieces of Brian's cage lie on the ground. Bobby is clinging onto a tree. He looks just like an old rug, he's feeling so battered. And there is Brian, comforting Mr Crackers. "Are you all right?" he asks in a worried tone. "I think so," says a shaky Mr Crackers. "Oh, I wouldn't be too sure of that," cries Endora, lifting her magic wand. Brian is afraid of what she might do next. "I must teach her a lesson, just like her cat." But it's too late! "I can't move," Brian tries to scream, but his lips remain silent. He hears Endora's voice at the back of his mind. "You asked for that, you dumb animal. I'm banishing you and your friend to 'nowhere' land. Then I can happily forget all about you!"

9 April

The empty quarter

Brian yawns, and pinches himself on his arm to make sure he's awake. "Where are we? This isn't a real place, is it Mr Crackers?" he asks his friend in a small, worried voice. Brian looks around nervously. "There's nothing here at all. It's completely empty. Not even a blade of grass!" Mr Crackers gives his feathers a shake, and peers at the emptiness that surrounds them. "Hmm, this is really strange. But it's not completely empty. Look over there!"
"What is it?" asks Brian.
"I think it's a door," replies Mr Crackers. "Let's see what's inside."
No sooner said than done. Brian bravely swings the door open wide. The two friends have been on the inside looking out. There's the most beautiful countryside outside!

10 April

A scarecrow

Mr Crackers flies onto Brian's shoulder and, together, the two friends look out across the landscape. "Let's keep this door open," suggests Mr Crackers. "If we shut it now, we'll never find it again." Brian is trying to be brave. He keeps peeping round the door to see what's happening. "Shut that door, can't you. There's a terrible draught here. Were you born in a barn or something?" a voice calls out. Brian jumps out of his skin. "Who's that?" he asks nervously. "Me, of course," the voice replies unhelpfully. "Shut that door, please. I'm freezing!" Brian peeps round the door again. The only thing he can see is a scarecrow, standing some distance away in the meadow. But surely scarecrows can't talk? "Why are you staring at me with such a silly expression on your face?" asks the scarecrow. "You can feel the draught the same as anyone." Brian doesn't know what to think. "This can't be true," he mutters.

11 April

Everything is possible here

"Everything is possible here," says the scarecrow. "So I see," says Mr Crackers. He perches on the scarecrow's shoulder. "Go away! Go away, you horrible bird! You're supposed to be frightened of me!" screams the scarecrow. "You shouldn't speak to my friend like that," growls Brian. "Oh, it's all right! Scarecrows are never polite to birds. They don't know any better," explains Mr Crackers. The scarecrow tries another angry look. But he suddenly begins to laugh when he sees it isn't working. Mr Crackers joins in. "What's your name?" he asks the scarecrow.

12 April

Ludwig

"My name's Ludwig," replies the scarecrow. "And who are you?" he asks. "This is my friend Brian, and I'm Mr Crackers." The three of them shake hands. "What are you doing here?" Ludwig asks. That, of course, is a very long story. When Brian finishes speaking, the scarecrow nods his head. "This is a case for Professor Warbler," he remarks sagely. "Who's he?" asks Brian, looking hopefully at Ludwig. "Can the Professor undo magic spells?" asks Mr Crackers. "No, I don't think so, but he always knows what to do," says the scarecrow. "And he's awfully good at inventions!" Ludwig starts to tell them about some of the Professor's ideas. Brian listens in amazement. "Now he's planning to fly round the world in a hot air balloon!" "Where does this Professor live?" Brian interrupts the scarecrow. "Perhaps we should go and see him." Ludwig looks doubtful. "It's rather a long way from here. But if you like, I'll take you to him."

13 April

A silly question?

Brian stares at Ludwig in surprise.
"Can you walk?" he asks the scarecrow.
"Of course I can walk," Ludwig replies.
"What a silly question!" Brian looks
confused. "It doesn't sound silly to me.
Scarecrows can't walk where I come from!"
Now it's Ludwig's turn to look surprised.
"That means I'd have to stay in the same
place all day long!" he exclaims. "How boring!"
Ludwig can't bear the idea of standing still.
"They can't even talk," adds Mr Crackers.
The scarecrow stares at his two new friends
in disbelief. "That's terrible!" he says. Then
he starts to stride up the hill. "Hurry up,
you two! Are you coming?" "Yes, yes, we're
on our way," pants Brian as he hurries
after the scarecrow.

14 April

Ludwig, the talkative scarecrow

Chatting happily together, the three of them set out on the long walk to Professor Warbler's house. Brian starts to feel hungry from all this exercise, but he doesn't like to say anything because Ludwig will keep on talking. "Do you always talk so much?" asks Mr Crackers suddenly. Ludwig looks surprised. "*Am* I talking too much?" he asks. "I'm sorry, but I don't often have anyone to talk to, so when I *do* find someone, I find it hard to stop. And ..."

"That's what I mean," Mr Crackers breaks in hurriedly. "My ears are feeling tired and I think Brian is hungry." "He does look miserable," replies Ludwig, pausing for a moment to look at the hungry bear. "Let's go and find my friend Ted the horse, and ask him for an apple."

15 April

Ted the lonely horse

Ted lives in an orchard. The three friends find him standing alone, with a woeful expression on his face, staring into the distance. "No one likes me," gulps Ted, "I feel so lonely." "What's all this about?" asks a brisk voice behind him. Ted turns his head and recognizes Ludwig. "No one likes me," he repeats, gazing at the scarecrow with his big sad eyes, "I feel ever so lonely." Ludwig tries to comfort his friend. He knows how much horses need a pal to keep them company. "You should never say things like that," says Ludwig, looking at him squarely in the eyes. "You *know* we all love you." But Ted looks sadder than ever. Mr Crackers starts to fidget. "Is he always such a miserable horse?" he asks. "No," replies Ludwig, with a frown. "He's just lonely."

16 April

Shaking

Brian has been gazing round the orchard. Suddenly his face brightens up. "I say, look at those apples!" he exclaims, stretching up to pick one. But the apples are out of reach. At last Ted begins to smile. Now he can be useful. "Move aside," he neighs at Brian and, pawing the ground with his hooves, he takes a running jump into the apple tree. And there he stays while he gets his balance. Then, using all his weight, he shakes the tree. "Enough for a tasty snack," he laughs, as the apples tumble to the ground. "I hope you're hungry!"

17 April

Apples

Apple dumpling, apple pie,
What a funny land I spy.
Apple crumble, apple sauce,
What a sad and lonely horse.

Apple sponge and apple cake,
What a lot of things I bake.
Eat an apple every day
To keep those winter colds at bay.

18 April

Brian can't count

Brian and Mr Crackers sit down and start crunching into Ted's delicious apples. "Don't *you* like apples?" Mr Crackers asks Ludwig with his mouth full. "I don't know. I don't need to eat, so I'm never hungry," replies the scarecrow. "Well *I am*!" laughs Brian. "I've eaten ten apples already!" Mr Crackers gives Brian a knowing look. "Only ten, you must be joking! I've counted fifteen at least ..." Brian looks rather cross. "Are you saying I can't count?" he demands. "Are you saying I'm greedy?" "Yes!" cries Mr Crackers. And everyone laughs as Brian takes a big bite from another apple.

19 April

Brian lies down for a nap

They all lie down for a rest. The sun is shining on Brian's head and his stomach is full of apples. "Where are you making for?" Ted enquires lazily. "We're on our way to see Professor Warbler," replies Ludwig. "We're looking for the frog princess. I'm hoping he'll help Brian and Mr Crackers." "You should get there before it's dark," says Ted. Ludwig nods his head. "Perhaps we could stay at Mr Pastry's house tonight," he suggests. "Pastry? What pastry?" asks Brian. Suddenly he's wide awake. "This pastry is able to walk and talk," neighs Ted. "You can't eat him!"

20 April

A strange place

"What a strange place," Brian murmurs to himself. "So this is 'nowhere' land." But he doesn't say anything because he doesn't want to upset the others. Mr Crackers winks at Brian. *He's* not sure what to make of it, either. Pastry men, flying horses, talking scarecrows ... Mr Crackers can hardly believe his senses. "It's time to go," says Ludwig, breaking the silence. So they all say good-bye to Ted and set off to reach Mr Pastry's house before nightfall.

21 April

Not like home

Brian looks around in wonder as the landscape slowly changes. "Everything is so different from home," he explains to Ludwig. "It's very beautiful, of course, but it's so different." Ludwig throws him an understanding look. "We're almost at Mr Pastry's house now," he says, gently. "We can have a good night's sleep. Tomorrow we must cross the abandoned wood and that can be very dangerous." Mr Crackers has flown on ahead to spy out the land. Now he returns. "There's a giant cake a little further on," he says excitedly. "I think it's a house or something." "That's where Mr Pastry lives," replies Ludwig. "Come on, Brian!"

22 April

Mr Pastry

Mr Pastry is standing outside his house to welcome our friends. "Hello, Ludwig," he greets the scarecrow, warmly. "Introduce me to your friends." "This is Brian and Mr Crackers," says Ludwig. "We're on our way to see Professor Warbler, and I was hoping we might stay the night. We don't want to cross the abandoned wood in the dark ..." "I should think not," interrupts Mr Pastry. "There are funny creatures in that wood. It's dangerous enough by day, let alone at night. You must be very careful." He looks seriously at Ludwig. "Hattie Hedgehog left the path once. She can't remember what happened, but nothing will make her return to that wood," continues Mr Pastry.

23 April

Too many apples

"Mr Pastry has baked us an apple tart for supper," Ludwig tells Brian. "I'd rather have a cream cake," replies Brian cheekily. "I think I've eaten too many apples today." Ludwig is rather annoyed that this is all Brian can say. "That's not very polite of you, Brian. Mr Pastry has done his best to make us welcome, and all you can do is complain." That evening, Brian sits in front of his apple tart with a nasty scowl on his face. "The whole house is made from cream, and what do we get? Apple tart!" grouches Brian, as he only takes one bite.

24 April

Brian learns his lesson

Mr Crackers almost falls off his perch when he hears Mr Pastry's shouts. "What's the matter?" Mr Crackers asks his friend. "Someone's eaten a large hole in my house!" wails Mr Pastry. Then Mr Crackers notices that part of the wall has disappeared. Ludwig comes running to find out what's happened. "Who did that?" he says furiously. They look at one another. "BRIAN!" they cry. Ludwig is the first to find the greedy bear. He's lying on the ground under a tree. Ludwig gives him an angry shake. "*You* ate a hole in the cake house!" he accuses his friend. "I feel so sick," is the only thing that Brian can say. "It's your own fault," says Mr Crackers. "I hope you've learned your lesson the hard way."

25 April

Setting to work

Mr Pastry's eyes are full of tears as he gazes at his house. "Don't be so upset, Mr Pastry," comforts Ludwig. "We'll help you mend your home." Mr Crackers and Ludwig set to work at once. They help Mr Pastry find all the ingredients he needs to make a cake. Then they stir the mixture until it is thick enough to make bricks, and they repair the wall like expert bricklayers. Before long the cake house is as good as new.

"It's high time we set off for the abandoned wood," says Ludwig. "Come on, Brian. We must be going." Brian is still feeling very sick, and he's feeling ashamed of himself for being so greedy. "I'm really sorry for what I did," he apologizes to Mr Pastry. "That's all right," says Mr Pastry kindly. "You're lucky to have friends like Ludwig and Mr Crackers. They've mended the wall." Brian agrees with him shyly. When they've all said good-bye to Mr Pastry, they set off for the abandoned wood.

26 April

The abandoned wood

It's not long before they reach the abandoned wood. "It doesn't *look* dangerous," remarks Brian. "That's what makes it so risky," answers Ludwig. "But I don't think much is likely to happen as long as we keep to the path." "Can I fly over it?" asks Mr Crackers. "I don't know," replies Ludwig. Chatting merrily to keep their spirits up, the three friends continue along the path. They don't notice that the path is getting narrower because they're so interested in what they are saying.

27 April

A very narrow path

Mr Crackers is the first to realize what's happening. He's noticed the path is getting narrower all the time. "I don't like the look of this," says Ludwig. "I think the trees must be moving!" "I think they're closing in on us," cries Brian, who has walked on ahead. "And it's getting darker and darker," cries Mr Crackers in alarm. "I don't like this at all," groans Ludwig. By this time, the path has become so narrow, they have to walk in single file. Ludwig is out in front, followed by Brian with Mr Crackers on his shoulder. "Be careful!" Ludwig suddenly warns Brian. "Look where you're going. It's not just the trees that are moving. Their roots are moving as well!"

28 April

A clearing

It's getting even darker in the wood. The trees are hanging so low over the path that Brian has to bend double to avoid their branches. Mr Crackers presses his claws deep into Brian's fur to stop himself falling from Brian's shoulder. "I can see light ahead," cries Ludwig suddenly, starting to walk a little faster. They come to a glade in the wood. At last, they can see sunlight again! Giant toadstools grow all around the edge of the clearing. Brian looks at them in amazement. "They're gigantic, aren't they?" cries Brian, and Mr Crackers nods his head in agreement.

29 April

A little rest

"We can rest here," says Ludwig. "Won't that be dangerous?" asks Mr Crackers nervously. Brian flops to the ground before Ludwig can reply. "I don't think so," says Ludwig, when he sees nothing happened when Brian sat down. Ludwig takes a large cloth from one of his pockets, and spreads it on the ground. "We can have our picnic now," says the scarecrow, producing a neat little parcel from another pocket in his jacket. Kind Mr Pastry has given them a fruit cake for their journey. "Oh dear, I can't bear to look at another cake," says Brian. "All the more for us," says Mr Crackers. And he tucks into his cake without another word.

30 April

A beautiful smell

"There's a beautiful smell here," remarks Brian. "I think it's coming from the giant toadstools." Ludwig glances behind him. "I don't know whether they're safe," says Ludwig. "I think we ought to get going." As Brian stands up, his attention is caught by something in the sky. "Now what are you staring at?" asks Ludwig impatiently. "I think we have a visitor," says Brian.

1 May

Pom

They all look up in alarm. There's a loud bang. "What on earth's that?" Brian asks Mr Crackers. Mr Crackers shrugs his shoulders. "We'll find out soon enough," he says. A strange object floats down towards them, and a small wheelbarrow falls at Brian's feet. Then a flying carpet lands in the clearing, and a little man crawls out. He's wearing a red pointed hat. "Hi!" says the strange little creature. "My name's Pom and I'm a gnome." "And what's that?" asks Brian, pointing at the carpet. "That's my flying carpet," replies Pom proudly. "I've had to make a crash landing because my engine stopped."

2 May

What a crash

Oh my goodness,
What a rumble!
Oh my goodness,
What a tumble!

Down it comes,
The flying carpet!
There sits Pom,
The clever pilot!

3 May

A piece of string

They all examine the carpet. "I don't think it's too bad," says Pom. "There's only a tear in the fringe, and the engine can be repaired." Pom begins to fiddle with the engine. "Has anyone got a piece of string?" he asks. "You could cut off a strip from my shirt," offers Ludwig. "It doesn't matter to me, I'm only a scarecrow." Pom tears a strip from Ludwig's shirt, and sets to work on the engine. "I'm on my way to see Professor Warbler to get a new part for my carpet," he tells them. "That's strange, so are we," says Mr Crackers. "Come with me," says Pom. "It'll be much faster than walking." Brian is not too sure. "Is there room for *all* of us?" he asks. "I can fly by myself!" cries Mr Crackers proudly.

4 May

All aboard

Brian and Ludwig step carefully onto the flying carpet. Pom starts the engine and, with a loud bang and a cloud of smoke, they take off from the clearing. Brian sits at the back and looks around nervously. He's a very heavy bear and he hopes the carpet will carry his weight. When he realizes all is well, he relaxes and starts to enjoy the flight. They fly over the abandoned wood and can see Professor Warbler's house in the distance. Pom doesn't fly too fast so Mr Crackers is able to keep up. "Isn't this fun," he chirps in delight.

5 May

Professor Warbler

"Hello, Pom," says Professor Warbler as the carpet lands in his garden. "I knew you were coming because I've invented a carpet detector! Let's go inside and have a cup of tea." He starts to press some buttons and turn all sorts of wheels in his kitchen, and finally pulls a huge lever. A machine starts to hum and the Professor disappears into his library. Brian stares round the kitchen. It's full of the weirdest devices! What a strange man the Professor is, thinks Brian.

6 May

All sorts of machines

"The Professor's house *is* weird," Brian whispers to Pom. "If you lived here, you'd soon get used to it," answers the gnome. "He's invented all these machines and he's always trying to improve them," he continues. "I'm always nervous when I come here because you never know quite what's going to happen." Ludwig laughs. "Sometimes he can't even remember his own name!" explains the scarecrow. "He's so absent-minded."
A machine is humming happily to itself in the corner. When the Professor comes back into the kitchen, he looks surprised to see our friends. "Oh yes," he says vaguely. "Visitors! I'd almost forgotten."

7 May

Tea and biscuits

"Why is the kettle on?" asks the Professor, looking at the machine in the corner. "Oh yes," he cries. "I was preparing tea for my visitors. How could I have forgotten!" He scratches his head and looks at our friends. "I don't think I know you," he says. He stares around the room curiously. Brian is examining a peculiar machine with all sorts of flashing lights. He notices the Professor watching him. "I could never understand anything like this," he says. The Professor smiles. "My friends, tea is ready and there are still some biscuits left over from this morning, so let's hurry to the table."

8 May

What an absent-minded professor!

"How is your flying carpet?" Professor Warbler asks
Pom when everyone is seated. Pom opens his mouth
to reply, but the Professor interrupts him. "Have
another biscuit, they're delicious, if I say so myself.
Perhaps I could invent a machine to make them."
Ludwig shouts with laughter. "You've already done it,"
he giggles. "Oh yes, so I have, I'm so forgetful.
Now what were we talking about?" asks the
Professor. "My flying carpet," Pom reminds him.
"Oh yes, how is it?" Brian and Mr Crackers look
at one another.
What an absent-minded professor!

9 May

The tele-mirror

After tea, the Professor gets down to work on the flying carpet. As he works, he tells our
friends about his latest invention. "It's called a tele-mirror!" When he has finished
repairing the carpet, the Professor goes across to an incredible machine, covered with
lamps and wires, with a mirror in the middle. "Stand back while I press this button," he
announces. "You'll soon see what my machine does." All kinds of whirring noises come
from the device. After a few seconds, a picture appears on the screen. Brian and Mr
Crackers recognize a familiar view. Suddenly, they see Miss Peggy on the screen, with
Beauty beside her.

Inventions take a long time

"Can we talk to her?" Mr Crackers asks hopefully. "No, I'm afraid not," the Professor replies, twiddling his moustache thoughtfully. "I must invent something else for that." Brian looks downcast. "Oh dear," he sighs. "We do need to speak to Miss Peggy. Could you possibly help us to get back home?" The Professor feels sorry for the bear because he looks so sad. He begins to twirl his moustache again, and his glasses nearly fall off the end of his nose. After a while he looks up. "Inventions take a long time, you know."

11 May

Stars and stripes

That evening, they all sit in front of the tele-mirror. The Professor is busy tuning the knobs on his machine. First of all, the screen shows Miss Peggy, then the frogs, then Farmer George and Bertie Beaver. They even spot Icicle the polar bear, as coloured stars and stripes dart across the screen. "The stars and stripes are caused by the wind," says the Professor. "I need to fix a larger umbrella on the roof to stop it spoiling the picture." Suddenly Endora appears on the screen. Brian's fur stands up on end. "There's that horrible witch again!"

12 May

Professor Warbler is bewildered

Ludwig turns to Brian in surprise.
"What's the matter?" asks the Professor. "That's the wicked witch who brought us to 'nowhere' land," cries Mr Crackers. "How nasty she looks!" exclaims Ludwig.
"She *is* nasty," says Brian. "Everyone is frightened of her. Look what she's doing now!" Professor Warbler is bewildered as he watches Endora.
"What on earth is she doing?" he wonders, twiddling his moustache.
"She must be brewing some new magic spell," thinks Mr Crackers, as he watches her stirring her cauldron.

13 May

What now?

Brian and Mr Crackers spend the night in the Professor's spare bedroom. Brian gets into bed while Mr Crackers makes himself comfortable on the window sill. "I'll just leave the window open," says Mr Crackers. "We might need to escape!" After all the adventures he's had, Mr Crackers has become very careful. But nothing happens that night, and the next morning the travellers are feeling strong again. The Professor is waiting for them to come down to breakfast. Brian looks happily at all the enormous spread on the table. After his fourth large glass of milk and his twelfth peanut butter sandwich (made with peanut butter from the Professor's own machine), Brian looks up from his breakfast. "And what now?" he asks.

14 May

The tele-telephone

"I've been thinking how I can convert my tele-mirror into a sort of tele-telephone. I've made a start on it already," says the Professor proudly, as he points to a tangled mass of wires in the corner of the room. "A very handy invention, if I may say so. I think I'm ready to try it out." He propels Brian towards it. "Here, try this on for size," he says as he hands the bear a helmet made from a soup pan. The helmet has lots of wires going into it, and a set of aerials pointing out from the sides. "Wait a minute, I'll help you put it on properly." The Professor pushes Brian into a chair and fits the tele-telephone over his ears. "Oh, how exciting!" cries Ludwig, as the others come over to watch.

15 May

Soup

Brian sits nervously in his chair, waiting to see what will happen. "It's rather a tight fit," he grumbles. "It's making my ears hurt." The Professor dismisses Brian's protest. "I can't help that, it's the biggest soup pan I could find. I gave it a good wash first," explains the Professor. "I think there's some soup left behind," giggles Ludwig. "It's dripping down Brian's nose." Brian scowls at Ludwig, but the Professor takes no notice. "A fantastic invention, if I may say so," he murmurs.

16 May

Hello, hello

Soup is dripping down the pan
Onto Brian's nose.
Our Professor beams with pride
While Brian's discomfort grows.

Can you hear me, are you there?
Is there any news?
I'm so glad to speak to you
Just to hear your views.

17 May

Boo!

The tele-telephone begins to hum.
Brian sits as quietly as he can, listening
carefully. "I can't hear anything," he
wails. "Shhh!" everyone mutters, while
Professor Warbler fiddles with the
knobs on his new invention. Suddenly
Bobby, the witch's cat, appears on the
screen. He's sitting on the tree trunk,
outside the Fieldmouse family home.
"Can he hear me?" whispers Brian.
The Professor nods his head. Brian
takes a deep breath and shouts "Boo!"
as loud as he can. Bobby, who
remembers Brian's roar only too well,
jumps up in alarm, and runs off with
his tail in the air as everyone bursts
out laughing.

18 May

Miss Peggy is surprised

Everyone is still enjoying the joke that Brian has played on Bobby. "Wow, that cat can certainly run!" sniggers Mr Crackers. The next person they see is Miss Peggy. She is looking extremely surprised. "Is that you Brian? Where are you Mr Crackers?" she calls. "You can't see us because we're with Professor Warbler in 'nowhere' land," hollers Brian. "You don't need to shout, I'm not deaf yet!" remarks Miss Peggy. "I didn't mean to shout," apologizes Brian. "But I'm so happy to talk to you again."

19 May

A long chat

"... and then that wicked witch, Endora, put a spell on us and now we're with Professor Warbler in 'nowhere' land," Brian tells Miss Peggy. "But we don't know what to do next. We need your help, Miss Peggy!" The old lady peers over the top of her glasses while she considers the problem. "You need some magic pondweed to save the frog princess and get yourselves back home," she says at last. "It grows by the fourth door to 'nowhere' land. I don't know where it is, so *you* will have to find it." Brian swallows his tears. He had hoped Miss Peggy could magic them home. Then he straightens his back like the courageous bear he is. "Then that's what we'll do," he says boldly.

20 May

The four doors

"Does anyone know where the fourth door is?" Brian asks hopefully. Ludwig shrugs his shoulders. "How would I know? I'm just an ordinary scarecrow," he mumbles. Pom doesn't know either. They all turn to Professor Warbler, who is lost in thought as usual. "I think the doors must be the ones that face the four winds," he murmurs. "Number one must face the north, number two the south, and number three the east. That means number four must be the door that faces the west wind," the Professor tells them. "Is it far away?" asks Brian.

21 May

A map

Professor Warbler goes over to a cupboard and takes out a map after a moment's searching. "Let's see where the west is," he says, as he unrolls the dusty map onto the table. Everyone looks at it curiously. "This map was drawn by my dear great-grandfather. He used to travel all over the world. He drew this map when he'd finished his travels. It's rather a splendid one, if I may say so." Brian blows the dust off the map and makes everyone sneeze. Atishoo! Atishoo-o!

22 May

That's where we must go

"He was a great artist, my great-grandfather. Look how beautifully he's drawn this map," the Professor says proudly. "Yes I know! But where's the fourth door?" asks Brian impatiently. "The fourth door? Oh yes, here it is!" says the Professor, as he points to a large cross on the edge of the map. "Isn't that a long way away?" asks Mr Crackers. "It's miles from here," answers Pom. "It's too far for my flying carpet!" The Professor stares at the map. "You must go through Circus Land, then sail over the sea until you reach the country of forests and deserts," he tells them. "At last, you will arrive at Wizard Gombal's castle. He lives near the fourth door, the door that faces the west wind." Brian pricks up his ears. "Wizard Gombal! Miss Peggy knows him. That's where we must go!" he cries. "It's going to take a long time to get there!" mutters Mr Crackers.

23 May

Another invention

The next day, Brian and Mr Crackers are busy getting ready for their journey. "Have you seen the Professor?" Brian asks his friend. "Yes, he's been busy in his laboratory all morning, but I don't know what he's up to. Shall we go and see?" All sorts of strange noises are coming out of the Professor's laboratory. "Good morning, my friends," he calls out in a cheerful voice. "Come in and see my latest invention. It's rather clever, if I may say so. This balloon will fly you wherever you need to go," the Professor tells them boastfully.

24 May

A balloon with a roof

Professor Warbler is standing beside some large pieces of cloth which are beginning to bulge and swell in all directions. The colourful balloon is soon so large, it fills the laboratory. Everyone runs outside and Brian stands in awe as he stares at the enormous monster. "How will you get the balloon out of your laboratory?" he asks the Professor. But the laboratory walls begin to crack before the Professor can answer. Brian steps back a few paces for safety. Suddenly the laboratory roof comes away, and the balloon carries it into the air. "That roof will keep out the rain on your journey!" exclaims the Professor. "Very ingenious, if I may say so."

102

25 May

Up into the sky

The Professor turns a handle which winds in the guide rope and hauls the balloon to safety. "Phew! That was hard work," he puffs. Now the sad time has come for saying goodbye. Ludwig stands rather awkwardly, while Pom fiddles with his wheelbarrow. Only the Professor is left talking excitedly. "Look, you just have to climb into this basket," he explains. "When you pull this rope it steers to the left. And when you pull this one, it steers to the right." But Brian isn't listening. It's so difficult saying goodbye to friends. "Now, do you understand what you have to do?" asks the Professor. "Yes, yes," answers Brian. "This one to go left, and this one ..." Then something unexpected happens. Brian has pulled the wrong rope and the balloon soars up into the sky.

26 May

A real problem

They all stare up into the sky. "He's taken off," cries Ludwig. "He's a born pilot, that bear," cries Pom enthusiastically. "I don't think he quite understood my instructions," says the Professor in alarm. "Nor do I," says Mr Crackers. "Goodbye my friends, I must be off or I'll never catch up with him!" And he quickly flies towards the balloon. Shaking his head, the Professor stares after them. "I only hope Brian manages to control the balloon," murmurs the Professor. At last, Mr Crackers catches up with his friend and lands on the edge of the basket. "What must I do now?" cries Brian. "The Professors *told* you. Weren't you listening?" asks Mr Crackers. "No, not exactly," answers Brian. "Now you have a real problem," says Mr Crackers. "You mean *we* are flying into problems," Brian corrects him. "Anyone would think you didn't have two good ears for listening!"

103

27 May

Above the clouds

As the balloon climbs higher and higher into the sky, Brian and Mr Crackers sit in the basket quarrelling. After a while, Brian shrugs his shoulders. "I don't want to argue any more," he says. "Neither do I," sighs Mr Crackers. "Can we be friends again?" asks Brian. Mr Crackers nods his head in relief.

"Let's see if we can control this balloon," suggests Mr Crackers. Brian points to one of the ropes. "I know what *this* one is for. It makes the balloon rise into the air," he says knowingly. "These ropes are for steering," Mr Crackers tells him. "But what do we do when we want to land? We're above the clouds now!" wails Brian, as he peeps over the edge of the basket. "I would never have believed it," he whispers fearfully.

28 May

Cheese or cheese

It's already beginning to get dark when Brian's stomach starts to rumble. "Perhaps there's something to eat, hidden away in this basket," suggests Mr Crackers. Brian looks in a sack and finds two cheese sandwiches. "Do you want a cheese sandwich or a cheese sandwich?" he asks Mr Crackers. "I think I'll have the one with the cheese in it," laughs Mr Crackers. When they've eaten their sandwiches, Brian settles down in a corner of the basket. "It's rather cold up here, isn't it, Mr Crackers? We can keep each other warm if we snuggle up together." Mr Crackers settles on Brian's shoulder. "And be more comfortable," he whispers into Brian's ear. "Mmm," mumbles Brian. "That bear can sleep anywhere," grumbles Mr Crackers. But Mr Crackers' eyes are closing. Soon the two friends are fast asleep on the first night of their journey.

29 May

Caw, caw!

"Caw, caw, caw!" Brian wakes up suddenly, feeling cold and stiff after a good night's sleep. "Caw, caw, caw!" "What? Where? Who?" cries Mr Crackers, waking from his dreams with a start. "Caw, caw! Who are you? Where are you going?" croaks a harsh voice. "And who are *you*?" asks Brian, looking at a large black bird sitting on the edge of the basket. "My name is Carl, Carl the raven," the bird introduces himself. "I'm Brian, and this is my friend Mr Crackers." Brian starts to tell their story, but Carl interrupts him. "I can smell cheese. Have you got any? It's my favourite food, you know." Brian looks at the newcomer rather huffily. "The cheese has all gone," he tells the bird crossly.

A thief

Carl behaves as if he hasn't heard a word Brian said. "I live in Circus Land, near the big circus," he tells Mr Crackers. "I should love to see a circus," sighs Mr Crackers wistfully. "Can we land the balloon?" Brian looks at him rather desperately. "Of course we can, but *how* do we do it?" Mr Crackers has no idea, but Carl ignores their dejected looks. "They have lovely cheese at the circus," he says, his bright eyes shining. "Sometimes I take a nice big piece." Brian stares at him in disbelief. "Do you steal it?" he asks. "You should pay for everything in Circus Land," replies Carl. "But I haven't got any money, so I pinch some food when I'm hungry." Brian catches the raven's eyes. "I don't agree with stealing," he says sternly, and Mr Crackers nods his head. "Isn't there any work for you?" Brian asks. "There is for bears, but have you ever seen a raven working in a circus?" Carl asks. Brian can't answer this question. He's never been to the circus.

31 May

Going down

"Look, there's the circus," cries Carl. Brian peeps over the edge of the basket and spots a brightly coloured tent below. "That's the Marisco Circus. They have the best cheese in the world," says the raven. Brian looks down longingly at the lively scene. "That's all very well, but we don't know how to land," he wails. "That's no problem," cries Carl, as he flies up to the canopy. Mr Crackers flies after him, and is just in time to see the raven peck at the balloon with his strong sharp beak. "What are you doing?" he asks frantically. "Brian can't fly!" But it's too late. The balloon collapses and falls from the sky. The basket crashes onto the ground and tips over. "You crazy raven, now look what you've done. Poor Brian!" cries Mr Crackers as he rushes to help his friend. "You did say you wanted to land," says Carl.

1 June

No problem

A balloon with a roof
Is a great way to fly.
If you know how to steer
You can travel the sky.

And if landing's a problem,
There's no need to shout.
The raven can burst it
And let the air out!

2 June

A little bruised

"What happened?" asks Brian in a confused voice. "Have you hurt yourself?" asks the worried Mr Crackers. But Brian doesn't hear his friend as he struggles shakily to his feet. "Did I pull the wrong rope again?" he asks Mr Crackers. "No, it was that stupid raven who burst the balloon with his beak." Brian looks at the raven, flying nervously above him. "Ohhhh!" is all that Brian can manage to say. He wriggles his claws and touches the bump on his head. "I'm bruised and battered, but nothing seems to be broken," he says.

3 June

Francisco Marisco

"Good afternoon everyone, perhaps I can help. Francisco Marisco at your service. I'm the ringmaster of the best circus in the world." Mr Crackers jumps with fright. He was so busy looking at Brian's bruises, he never heard the man's approach. "This is really amazing," Francisco continues. "I can see it all. Enormous posters saying, *Come and see the bravest bear in the land. Only appearing at the Marisco Circus.* Would you like a job?"

4 June

Perfect, perfect

Brian stares at Francisco in amazement. "Do you mean *me*?" he says. "Of course! Can you see another bear? cries the ringmaster. "But I don't know anything about circuses," replies Brian. "And we're on our way to the fourth door," Mr Crackers joins in. "And then we must rescue the frog princess."

Francisco Marisco looks at Mr Crackers. "Are you two travelling together?" he asks. The two friends nod their heads. "Perfect, perfect! This is even better. I can see it all now ..." cries Francisco.

5 June

Cheese for Carl

Carl has been sitting quietly, listening to Francisco. "See, what did I tell you?" he cries out suddenly. "There's never any work for *me*! How am I going to earn my living? It's always outsiders who get the best jobs, while the poor local ravens can only *dream* of cheese!" Mr Crackers looks at Carl crossly. "Brian can't help being a bear," he says. "I suppose you're right," Carl replies grudgingly. "But I would love some cheese." Brian feels sorry for the raven. "You can have *my* cheese if you like. I'd much rather have honey and cake." The ringmaster comes to a decision. "That settles it," he cries. "A pot of honey and a cake every time you perform." Brian grins. "And cheese for Carl?" he asks. "As much as he can eat," replies the ringmaster.

6 June

Why are they in cages?

They all set off in the ringmaster's car. Gigantic posters advertise the Marisco Circus all along the road. After a while, they come to the town and Brian finds himself staring at the biggest, brightest circus tent in the world. It's surrounded by caravans and trailers. "Why are those animals in cages?" asks Brian. He remembers the time he was trapped in a cage by that wicked witch Endora. "They're only wild animals," explains Francisco. "And wild animals can be dangerous. But you would have your own caravan, with everything you need." Mr Crackers looks at the animals and decides he doesn't trust Francisco.

7 June

Mick the clown

"Here are your quarters for the night," says Francisco, with a flourish. "You can share a caravan with Mick the clown. He's a very jolly person, as you'll soon find out." The ringmaster has no sooner spoken than Mick appears, walking on his hands. Brian isn't sure whether he should stand on his head to say hello. But before he can decide, Mick springs to his feet. "Hello, I'm Mick," he says. Brian and Mr Crackers stare at his painted face in surprise. "I'm so good at making people laugh, they have no time to cry," he explains. "Oh, I understand," cries Brian. "You do look very funny."

8 June

Brian is nervous

That evening, the three new friends are sitting in Mick's caravan, when the clown saunters in. "Hello, my balloonists, everything okay?" he asks cheerily. Brian looks up from his bowl of honey. "Mmmm, this honey is delicious," he says. "And so is this cheese," croaks Carl. Mick glances at Brian. "You'd better get a good night's sleep, because you've got your first performance tomorrow." Brian looks at the clown in horror. "What do I have to do?" he asks. "I've never performed in a circus before, and I'm awfully nervous!"

9 June

A slap on the shoulder

Brian can't get to sleep. He keeps thinking about his performance. Suppose it's a disaster! But at last he falls asleep. Soon he's dreaming he is the star of the circus. The audience clap and cheer for more, and the ringmaster slaps him on the shoulder because he's so pleased with his performance. But then he suddenly realizes that someone is trying to rouse him. "Wake up, it's time for your rehearsal," says a deep voice. Brian drowsily opens his eyes and sees a stranger standing by his bed.

Bozo, the animal tamer

"My name's Bozo, the animal tamer," says the big man in a gruff voice. "Enough of all this laziness! It's time to rehearse your performance. Today's your big day!" Brian rubs the sleep out of his eyes. "My name's Brian," says the bear. "I don't need to be tamed! Just tell me what to do." Bozo scowls. "Bears are wild animals, and bears need taming," splutters Bozo. He flips a large whip from behind his back, and cracks it under Brian's nose. Brian throws Bozo a furious look. "That isn't necessary!" he exclaims. "I knew there was something fishy going on," Mr Crackers whispers in Brian's ear. Bozo produces a large ball. "I want you to learn to balance and walk on this ball," he says.

11 June

Walking on a ball

Brian stares at the ball. "Have I got to walk on that?" he asks in dismay. "It'll roll away, and I'll fall over!" Bozo frowns at him impatiently. "That's why you've got to learn how to keep your balance!" he growls. Brian tries to climb on the ball, but it rolls away. He tries again, and again, but he can't manage it. Bozo gets angrier and angrier. "You stupid bear, it isn't that difficult," he roars in a rage. Mr Crackers can't restrain himself any longer. "If you're so good at it, why don't you show us how it's done!" he says furiously. Bozo walks over to the ball and tries to get on. But the ball rolls away, and he falls over. "It's not so easy after all, is it?" grunts Brian.

114

Well done!

Bozo knows he has made himself look stupid, so he starts to be more friendly. At last, Brian manages to climb onto the ball, but it's so difficult for him to keep his balance. Eventually, he tastes success and moves the ball a short distance. Francisco has been watching the bear. "Well done, Brian!" he cries, clapping his hands. Mr Crackers feels so proud of his friend. Carl is pleased everything is working out, because he wants his cheese breakfast.

13 June

Something very special

"And now for something very special!" cries Francisco. "I've had a splendid car built for my performing bear. Come and look at it." They spot the red sports car standing in the ring the moment they enter the tent. Brian stares at it in disgust. "I'll never fit into that!" he exclaims. "Oh, but you will, Mr Bear," says Francisco Marisco. "Otherwise you'll have to go on a diet," threatens Bozo. Brian gives Bozo a furious look. "I'm not fat," he protests as he climbs into the little car. Unfortunately, his paw jabs down the accelerator by mistake, and the car shoots forward with a burst of speed.

14 June

A driving lesson

"Wow! that's fast," thinks Mr Crackers. Brian is beginning to enjoy himself and drives round the ring like a racing driver. "Yippee!" cries Brian happily, as everyone jumps out of his way. He jabs at the accelerator again, but the engine coughs and begins to splutter, and then it slows to a halt. Brian sits at the steering wheel, and shrugs his shoulders. "It won't go any further," he complains. "What do you expect?" laughs Mr Crackers. "I think you need some driving lessons."

15 June

It's going to be a fantastic show

"There's nothing to worry about," cries Francisco Marisco. "I think it's run out of gas. But we'll fill the tank for this evening. It's going to be a fantastic show. Let's drink to our success," and they all go off to the ringmaster's caravan. Francisco gives everyone a glass of lemonade. Brian bursts with pride as they congratulate him. Bozo smiles as he sips his drink. Even Carl crows about Brian's heroic deeds, and he hates lemonade!

16 June

Brian's heroic deeds

Walking on a big round ball,
Driving round the ring.
Brian isn't scared at all,
He can do anything!

He's our hero, he's so brave,
Everyone agrees.
He can do all sorts of things
With amazing ease.

17 June

Mr Crackers investigates

Brian takes a nap in the afternoon to prepare himself for his performance. Mr Crackers isn't tired. In fact, he's longing to find out more about Francisco Marisco's circus. He flies into the big tent and perches on the ridge pole. Now he can watch everything that's going on. There's a great hustle and bustle. Everyone is busy getting ready for tonight's show. But Mr Crackers is more interested in the wild animals and he decides to fly over to their cages. He lands outside the largest cage and peeps through the bars. "Who are you?" asks Mr Crackers shyly.

18 June

A loud roar

His answer is a loud roar. "Oh, I see, you're the lions," apologizes Mr Crackers, as he finds himself staring into a lion's mouth. "Do calm down, please," he pleads. "I belong to the circus, too. My friend is Brian the bear. He's the new star of the circus." The lion gives Mr Crackers a long, hard stare. "That changes everything," he roars, as his scowl subsides, and he goes to sit beside another lion in the corner of the cage.

19 June

Dangerous lions

"You don't seem fierce to me," says Mr Crackers. "No we're not," replies the lion. "But if we don't look fierce, we would lose our jobs in the circus." Mr Crackers nods his head. "What happens when you perform?" he asks. "We pretend to be very dangerous indeed! But we'd like to teach that Bozo a lesson. That whip of his can really hurt," grumbles the lion.

20 June

A friendly elephant

Mr Crackers says goodbye to the lions. Then he spots an elephant and decides he wants to talk to him, too. Mr Crackers flies across to the elephant and perches on his trunk. "What do *you* do in the circus?" he asks. "I walk round the ring with a tiger on my back, and then I rear up on my hind legs," replies the elephant. "But the best bit is when I sit on a stool." Mr Crackers looks at the elephant's gigantic body. "It must be a strong stool," laughs Mr Crackers.

21 June

A heap of clothes

Mr Crackers spends the afternoon getting to know all the animals in the circus. When he gets back to the caravan, he finds Brian pacing up and down outside. "Where have you been all afternoon?" asks Brian peevishly. "It wasn't very kind of you to leave me all alone. You're supposed to be my friend!" he whimpers. Mr Crackers bites back an indignant reply. He realizes Brian is feeling nervous about the show. "What's that?" Mr Crackers asks, pointing to a heap of clothes. "That's my costume for tonight, but I'm not sure if I like it," complains Brian crossly.

22 June

Very smart

Crackers looks at the pile of clothes. There's a jacket, a bow-tie, and a pair of enormous shoes. Mr Crackers points to a hat, decorated with flowers. "I don't think I could wear that hat," he chuckles. "And those shoes! But you could try the jacket and the bow-tie. They're very dashing." Brian glances at Mr Crackers suspiciously. "Do you think they're smart, or are you joking?" he asks. "No, I mean it," replies Mr Crackers. Brian puts on the jacket and the bow-tie. Then he looks at himself in the mirror. "Perhaps you're right," he admits. "Okay, I'll wear the jacket, but you can forget the rest!"

23 June

Brian puts his foot down

It's rather a tough job convincing Francisco and Bozo: the ringmaster and the animal tamer do all they can to persuade Brian to wear his costume. "Look, we're doing you a favour giving you an outfit like this. Only a great star would be allowed to wear it," urges Francisco, trying to talk Brian into changing his mind. "At least wear the shoes," pleads Bozo. But Brian puts his foot down. When it's clear he won't go ahead with his performance, the ringmaster finally gives in. "Okay, just the jacket and the bow-tie," he grumbles.

24 June

What a lot of people

Slowly the circus tent fills with people. Everyone in Circus Land has come from near and far to see the new star. They've never seen a bear before! Francisco Marisco rubs his hands eagerly. This show will be a real money-spinner. Brian peers out from behind the curtain. "What a lot of people!" gasps the bewildered bear. "Yes, and they're all here to see *you*," booms Bozo's voice. "So mind you don't disappoint them!"

25 June

Ladies and Gentlemen!

When the audience has taken their seats, Francisco Marisco strides into the ring. "Ladies and Gentlemen! Tonight we have a treat in store. Our celebrity cast includes Mick the clown and Bozo, the man who will enter the lions' cage with only his whip to protect him. Take my word for it, they are the fiercest lions in the land!" Mr Crackers raises an eyebrow. "Oh, yes," he thinks, "*really* fierce." The ringmaster is well into his stride. "And then we have our star act, Brian the bear. But first, a round of applause for Jacko the sealion!"

26 June

Jacko

"Oink, oink!" cries Jacko the sealion, as he waddles into the ring. He claps his fins together in time with the music and bows to acknowledge the audience's cheers. Jacko throws a beach ball into the air with a flourish, and catches it on the end of his nose. Then he parades around the ring, to the delight of the audience. "Oink, oink!" he cries, as he leaves the ring to the sound of applause.

27 June

I can do better

Mick runs into the ring and takes a bow. He produces a tennis ball from his pocket. "Anything Jacko can do, I can do better," he cries, as he spins the ball on his finger. The audience laughs. Then Mick drops the ball, trips over his feet, and cries buckets of tears. When the clown manages to play a tune on his tiny trumpet, the audience cheers.

28 June

Is it on the programme?

Brian and Mr Crackers are watching the show from behind the curtain. They marvel at the daring acrobats, the clever jugglers and, of course, the stunts of the other animals. The terrified audience watches Bozo as he puts his head inside a lion's mouth. When the lion spots Mr Crackers, he winks and half closes his jaws. The audience holds its breath. Bozo yanks his head out of the lion's mouth, and cracks his whip noisily. The audience claps and cheers. But when Mr Crackers notices Bozo's white face, he knows *that* trick wasn't part of the programme!

29 June

Good luck, Brian

At last, the time has come for Brian
to enter the spotlight. "Good luck!"
Mr Crackers breathes, as the drums
roll. Brian goes into the ring with
Bozo. The audience is hugely impressed.
"What a big bear!" they whisper
to each other. "He looks really strong!"
Brian puffs out his chest to make himself look
larger. And when Bozo rolls the ball over to him,
Brian jumps onto it with ease.
He even manages to stay on
board all round the ring.
"What a talented bear
I am," thinks Brian.

30 June

What excitement!

Next, Brian gets into his little red car.
But what's Bozo doing? He has placed
a large hoop in the centre of the ring.
Now he's setting fire to it. The audience
holds its breath, this is really exciting!
Brian isn't at all pleased. He's afraid of fire,
but he can't stop now because Bozo
is cracking his whip. "Okay mate!"
thinks Brian. "I'll do it just this once,"
he vows. "But this is definitely the last
time!" Brian starts the car and circles
the ring. Then he speeds towards the
burning hoop and, with his eyes
tightly shut, he drives straight through it.
"Bravo! Well done!" the audience cries,
applauding, as Brian marches
angrily out of the ring.

125

1 July

Brian's revenge

The circus is over and the audience is going home. Everyone is talking about Brian the bear. It was the best show they've ever seen! Brian is fuming. "What a dirty trick!" he mutters. He's determined to get his own back on Francisco and Bozo. The two men are busy putting the lions back into their cage. "We'll see about this," mutters Brian. And before anyone realizes what is on his mind, Brian has pushed the ringmaster and the animal trainer into the lions' cage and locked them in. Francisco and Bozo shake the bars. "Help! Let us out!" they cry. A crowd gathers in front of the cage, but no one lifts a finger to let them out. They're too busy laughing. "Serves them right!" grunts Brian.

2 July

As punishment

As punishment, they're made to spend
The whole night in the cage.
The lions get a pile of hay;
While the two men froth and rage.

Next morning, they'll be released,
But Brian will have gone.
He doesn't want to play with fire;
He'll be on his way by dawn.

126

3 July

Another goodbye

Brian and Mr Crackers decide to leave the circus at first light the next morning. Mick the clown is very sorry to see them go, and so is Carl. "That's the end of my cheese!" croaks the raven. Brian and Mr Crackers have a long journey ahead of them. Everyone comes to wave them off and to wish them a safe journey. Except, of course, for Francisco and Bozo! They're still locked in the lions' cage. "We'll get you for this!" they scowl, as the two friends leave the circus.

4 July

Ready for a picnic

"Haven't we walked far enough for now?" Brian asks Mr Crackers. "Mick gave us some lovely cakes, and I'm ever so hungry!" Mr Crackers looks at his friend. "You're *always* thinking about food," he groans. "It's all right for you to talk, you just sit on my shoulder!" grumbles Brian. Mr Crackers sees Brian's point. "Okay," he agrees. "Let's have a rest and eat those cakes." And the two friends find a shady spot for their picnic.

5 July

Where's Mr Crackers?

Brian spreads a large cloth on the ground, and gets out Mick's honey cakes. "They look delicious, don't they?" he asks Mr Crackers. But there's no reply. Brian looks for his friend, but he's nowhere to be seen. Mr Crackers has vanished! When there's only one honey cake left, Brian starts to feel worried. Where's Mr Crackers?

6 July

Never far away

Brian feels scared, and that's not very pleasant, not even for a bear like Brian! Then he hears voices in the distance. "There you are!" he says in relief, as he recognizes his friend's voice. "Mr Crackers never disappears for long. He knows how much I miss him." Mr Crackers perches on a branch, just above his friend's head. "Look, I've saved you a cake," says Brian.

129

Snuffles

"One cake isn't much, especially when we have a visitor," grumbles Mr Crackers. "A visitor?" I can't see anyone," exclaims Brian. "Look behind you!" says Mr Crackers. Brian turns round, and sees a large, scruffy dog. "I didn't hear you coming," he apologizes. "You were too busy eating those cakes," barks the dog. Brian doesn't know what to say. Mr Crackers comes to his rescue. "This is Snuffles, the best tracker dog in Circus Land," he says, as he introduces the visitor.

Not for anything

"What does a tracker dog do?" asks Brian. "Whatever you want me to," replies Snuffles. "I can track down anything, from your friend here to a lost handkerchief!" Brian is amazed. "Are you looking for someone at the moment?" he asks carefully. "Of course! Francisco Marisco asked me to find a large bear and a bird, and take them back to the circus," replies Snuffles importantly. "You don't need to look any further!" says Brian bravely. "But we're not going back to that circus, not for anything in the world!" he splutters angrily.

9 July

Forget it!

Mr Crackers chokes back his laughter. When Brian gets angry, he gets *really* angry. "Just like a bear!" giggles Mr Crackers. Snuffles is confused. "But listen," he tries to explain, but Brian doesn't want to hear. "We're not going back, whatever you say! And you can tell that Francisco to drive through the burning hoop himself!" growls Brian. Snuffles makes one last attempt. "They'll think I'm no good at my job if I go back alone," he pleads. "Well, you *did* find us. But as for going back, you can forget it!" says Brian.

10 July

Back alone

"You can have my cake to cheer yourself up," Mr Crackers tells the dog. "I've just had a snack, so I'm not very hungry." Snuffles gobbles the little cake whole. He licks his lips as the last crumb disappears. "Well, I suppose I must go back on my own," he sighs, looking hopefully at Brian and Mr Crackers. The two friends shake their heads. "Our journey takes us in the opposite direction," says Brian.

11 July

Seagulls

Mr Crackers has flown on ahead, leaving Brian all on his own. Suddenly, he reappears and perches on Brian's shoulder. "Can you hear that?" he whispers. "I can't hear anything," replies Brian. "Look up into the sky," says Mr Crackers. "All I can see is birds," answers Brian. He can't understand why his friend is so excited. "They're *seagulls*!" cries Mr Crackers. "Are they friends of yours?" asks Brian. "No, you idiot," answers Mr Crackers. "But the ocean can't be far away if there are seagulls around!"

12 July

The ocean

The two friends have reached the top of the next hill. Brian can hardly believe his eyes as he glimpses the ocean beneath him. He's never seen anything like it. "I can't see the other side," he gasps to Mr Crackers. "Of course you can't! It's the ocean, not a lake or a river," explains Mr Crackers. "I've never seen the ocean myself, but I've been told about it by my friend, the snowgoose. He flies across the ocean every year, and knows all about it!" Brian can hardly take it in. "And what are those?" he asks his friend, pointing at the waves. Mr Crackers can't help laughing. "They're waves, you idiot!" Brian is very impressed, and slowly walks down to the beach.

132

13 July

Cold and salty

Brian steps warily into the water. "Brrrr, it's freezing!" he exclaims. Then he bends down to have a drink. "Yuk, it's salty!" he cries, as he spits out the water. Now it's Mr Crackers' turn to look surprised. Salty? The snowgoose didn't tell him the water tastes salty. "I wonder what else the ocean has in store?" he wonders.

Brian looks along the beach, and out over the ocean. "Can you see any boats?" he asks his friend. "No," replies Mr Crackers. "But I *can* see a hut over there. Let's go and have a look."

14 July

A funny poster

When Brian and Mr Crackers reach the hut, they see a poster nailed to a post. "If the boat is not here, it's on a trip. Please wait until it returns," it reads. "What a funny thing to say," laughs Mr Crackers. Brian goes into the hut to look around. He's hoping to find something to eat. He spots a bottle of lemonade on the table. "Hurrah!" he exclaims. "That's just what I need to get rid of the taste of salt water." Brian drinks the lemonade. "I think I'll have a nap while we wait for the boat," Brian tells Mr Crackers. Before Mr Crackers can reply, Brian is snoring peacefully.

15 July

The boat comes in

Brian is woken by a dreadful noise. "What's that?" he groans, holding his head in his paws. "I've never heard anything like it!" "The boat's here!" calls Mr Crackers. Brian runs outside to have a look. He can see the boat clearly now. The engine shudders noisily as steam billows out of the funnel. "What a racket it makes," grumbles Brian. "It's giving me a headache." The boat draws closer to the shore. "Look! There's the captain standing on deck," cries Mr Crackers.

16 July

Look, there's the steamer

Look, there's the steamer out at sea,
It sails from land to land.
And there's the captain on the deck,
With a hook for his hand.

Look, here's the steamer drawing near,
It sails with the tide.
And here's the captain on the deck,
It's time for Brian to hide.

17 July

Captain Ironhook

When the boat has reached its moorings, the captain drops anchor. Then he pulls a lever to release the gangplank. "Ahoy there!" shouts the captain. "Come on board." Brian and Mr Crackers make their way gingerly along the gangplank. "Good afternoon, my friends! My name is Ironhook," the captain greets them, as they arrive on board. Brian and Mr Crackers look at him cautiously. He's wearing a black patch over his right eye, and instead of his left hand, there's an iron hook! "That's odd!" think Brian and Mr Crackers.

18 July

A pirate

The captain smiles at his guests,
and his smile makes him look rather spiteful.
"Haven't you seen a pirate before?" he asks
the two friends. What's that? A pirate? Even
Brian starts to feel scared. Captain Ironhook notices
Brian's expression. "Don't be afraid," he cries.
"I've changed my job! Where do you want to go?"
Brian and Mr Crackers can hardly believe their luck.
Here's someone to help them. "We're on our way to
visit Wizard Gombal," begins Brian, but the captain
interrupts him. "Okay, you can tell me
all about it later. Let's get the boat moving."

19 July

Weighing anchor

"You weigh anchor while I pull in the gangplank," Captain Ironhook orders Brian. The bear looks at the captain in surprise. "Weigh the anchor? What do you mean?" Brian asks. "Why do you want me to weigh the anchor? I've never heard such nonsense!" The captain stares at Brian. "Are you trying to be funny?" he demands sternly. Brian shakes his head and blushes. The captain stares at Brian again, and then he bursts out laughing. "What a landlubber you are! Weighing anchor means hauling it in," he chortles. Poor Brian! He doesn't know where to look, and his face turns an even brighter red from embarrassment.

20 July

Buried treasure!

Brian and Mr Crackers join the captain in his cabin. "How long does the crossing take?" asks Brian. "It usually takes three days," replies Captain Ironhook. "But it'll take longer this time. I've got to dig up my buried treasure!" Mr Crackers can hardly believe his ears. "Treasure, *real* treasure?" he cries in a startled voice. "Where did you get it from?" The captain gives Mr Crackers a lofty stare. "I stole it when I was a pirate," he replies in a matter of fact tone. Brian doesn't like the sound of this at all, but he keeps quiet. It's a long way to the shore and Brian doesn't like swimming!

21 July

Jump to!

Brian is sitting happily on deck, enjoying the evening sunshine. "Jump to, landlubbers! That's enough lazing around," barks out the captain. "We've got to eat, then it'll be time to turn into our bunks." Brian looks uneasy. "What are bunks?" he asks in a worried voice, thinking they might be cages. The captain looks at Brian in surprise. "You silly landlubber!" he cries. "That's what sailors call their beds," he chuckles.

22 July

Sea legs

"Why do sailors call everything by different names?" Brian mutters to himself. "It makes life so difficult for a simple bear like me!" When they have eaten their supper, the captain shows the two friends to their cabin. Captain Ironhook is already at the wheel when they appear on deck next morning. "Hi there, landlubbers!" he greets Brian and Mr Crackers. "Did you sleep well?" Brian's face has turned rather green. "I feel sick," he groans. "Don't worry," the captain replies. "You haven't got your sea legs yet, but you'll find them soon."

138

Morris

Brian starts up from his midday nap. "Who was that?" he asks Mr Crackers. "I don't know, I was asleep too," replies his friend. They look round in surprise. Where did that voice come from? Suddenly, a fish appears alongside the boat. "Hi there!" calls the fish. "My name's Morris. Who are you?" Brian rubs his eyes in amazement, and Mr Crackers' beak falls open. Have you ever heard of a flying fish? The two friends have just seen one!

24 July

The first time

"My name's Brian, and this is my friend, Mr Crackers," says the bear. "Pleased to meet you both, I'm sure," replies Morris. "Excuse me a moment," he gasps, as he disappears into the sea. After a while, the fish returns. "Here I am again," Morris calls cheerily. "Fish have to breathe under water, you know." Brian nods his head. "Yes, but it's the first time I've ever seen a fish *flying*!" he chuckles. Then Mr Crackers joins in. "Let's fly together," he suggests, "and have a chat on the way."

25 July

Birds are lucky

Morris and Mr Crackers have lots of fun flying round and round the boat. Brian waves to them each time they pass, but he feels rather gloomy. He's sad he can't fly with them. "Birds are so lucky," he thinks to himself. "Why can't I have wings?" Brian's eyes close and he dreams that he's flying with Morris and Mr Crackers.

26 July

Snapper

"All hands on deck!" shouts Captain Ironhook into Brian's ear, wakening him from his dreams. "What is it?" Brian asks in alarm, but the captain doesn't answer. He's busy staring at the horizon. "Where's your little friend? We're nearing my treasure island." Brian points to Mr Crackers. "He's up there with Morris," the bear replies. A deep frown appears on the captain's forehead. "Morris, eh? That means Snapper can't be far behind." Brian looks puzzled. "Who's Snapper?" he asks. "He's the biggest shark you've ever seen!" replies the captain.

27 July

Keep away

"A shark? What's a shark?" asks Brian. "Sharks can be very nasty creatures," explains Captain Ironhook. "And Snapper is the biggest and nastiest shark I know." The captain looks sadly at the hook he uses for his left hand. "When Snapper bites, he has no pity." Brian looks at the captain's arm in alarm. "Did Snapper do that to you?" he asks. "Yes, my friend, he did." replies the captain. "Be sure to keep away from him, he's a very dangerous shark!"

28 July

What colossal teeth!

Mr Crackers flies back on deck and hears the last part of their chat. He perches on Brian's shoulder and preens his feathers. "I don't think Snapper is *that* dangerous," he says. "As long as you don't do anything to annoy him." The captain's face turns an angry red. "Have you spoken to that monster?" he asks Mr Crackers. "Where is he? I want to teach him a lesson!" Mr Crackers looks at the captain thoughtfully. "Snapper is swimming next to the boat," he announces. Captain Ironhook and Brian look over the rails. Sure enough, they soon spot the enormous shark swimming beside the boat. He stares back at the captain with a cruel smile on his face. Brian steps back in horror. "What colossal teeth!" he exclaims.

Your own fault

"Hello, Captain Ironhook," Snapper calls out. "Do you remember me?" The captain's face turns purple. "Do I *remember* you?" he explodes. "I have you to thank for this!" he cries, waving his hook. "You ate my hand!" Snapper smiles his cruel smile. "No, I didn't," the shark replies. "I spat it out as soon as I could," he chortles. "Anyway, it was your own fault. You shouldn't have made me so angry." And he tells Brian and Mr Crackers how the captain tried to harpoon him. "That wasn't a very nice thing to do," splutters Brian. "That would have made me angry, too." Mr Crackers thinks the same.

30 July

Run aground

"Watch out!" cries Snapper, but it's too late. Captain Ironhook has not been paying attention, and his boat has run aground. It grinds to a shuddering halt, and everyone falls over. "A thousand cable-hawsers!" curses the captain. "What's happened?" gasps Brian. "Don't worry, there's no damage to the boat," cries Snapper. "But it *is* stuck in the sand. I'll help you to pull it free again." Everyone is relieved that it's not too serious. "Then let's go and find my treasure!" announces the captain.

31 July

The treasure map

Captain Ironhook spreads his treasure map on the sand. "Mmmm, now let me see," he mumbles. "Thirty paces forward, now ten paces to the left," mutters the captain, walking up the beach. "Another ten paces forward, and now twenty paces to the right. Yippee! This is it!" he declares.

1 August

The treasure chest

Brian and Mr Crackers look at the captain. He's standing under a giant palm tree. Bunches of coconuts hang among its leaves. "Let's get to work," orders the captain. He's brought a large spade with him, and he starts to dig with a will. After a while, Brian and Mr Crackers hear the spade hit something hard under the sand. They help the captain lift a huge chest out of the ground. It's a beautiful chest, circled with iron bands. Captain Ironhook takes an ancient key out of his pocket, and unlocks the chest. It's crammed with gold and jewels. "Oh, what beautiful treasure! I've never seen anything like it," cries Brian.

2 August

So much treasure!

Silver and gold
In an ancient chest.
Jewels from the east
And gems from the west.

144

Captain Ironhook is happy

"It's all still here," sighs the captain, examining his treasure chest. "I can buy a new boat at last!" he cries, as he dances a little jig in triumph. Then he locks the chest again. "Come on, you lazy landlubber! Give me a hand," he shouts. Brian helps the captain heave the chest on board the boat. When it's safely stored in the captain's cabin, they join Mr Crackers on deck. "We'll have a party this evening," cries the captain. "Then tomorrow we'll continue our journey."

4 August

Freeing the boat

Captain Ironhook stands at the wheel while Brian hangs over the side. He's not going to miss this! Snapper has a strong rope between his teeth. He's trying to pull the boat free. Mr Crackers and Morris fly above Snapper, encouraging him to pull harder. Suddenly Brian feels the boat start to move. Everyone laughs with relief. "Now we can sail across the ocean again," cries Captain Ironhook.

5 August

Seasick

There is a strong wind, and the boat bobs up and down wildly on the frothy waves. Brian looks very sorry for himself. Mr Crackers comes flying up to him. "Land ahoy, land ahoy!" he cries, as he lands on Brian's shoulder. "I can see land on the horizon," squawks Mr Crackers excitedly. "I think we're almost there." Brian looks relieved. "I'm glad of that," he mutters. "I feel so seasick. I'll be glad to walk on firm ground again."

6 August

Nearing land!

Mr Crackers searches for Captain Ironhook. "Where's the captain?" he asks Brian. "I think he's down below," replies his friend. "Let's go and warn him we're nearing land. I don't want to run aground again!" says Brian with a shudder. "Ho, ho, landlubbers! I know land's in sight," booms the captain's voice behind Brian's ear. "You don't trust this old sea dog, do you? Just one little slip, and you expect me to do it again," Captain Ironhook grumbles, as he goes to stand at the boat's wheel.

147

7 August

Good-bye

Brian and Mr Crackers wave good-bye to the captain. "Farewell, landlubbers!" Captain Ironhook cries from his boat. "Have a good journey, and mind how you go." Morris waves good-bye, too. And then, with a cheerful flip of his tail, he disappears beneath the waves to look for his friend Snapper. "We're alone again," sighs Brian, standing on the shore. "I wonder what will happen next?" Mr Crackers perches on Brian's shoulder. "At least we'll keep warm," he replies. "It's so hot here!" He gives Brian a large red handkerchief. "It's a present from the captain," he says.

8 August

A desert

Brian and Mr Crackers see fewer and fewer trees and bushes as they leave the ocean behind them. The landscape is turning into a desert. There's not a cloud in the sky and Brian is feeling thirsty. "I think I'll see if I can find a shady spot," says Mr Crackers, as he flies on ahead. Brian tries to keep up with his friend. "All this sand and heat is too much for a bear," he pants.

9 August

Mr Crackers has a bath

Mr Crackers flies off as Brian struggles on through the sand. What's that? Mr Crackers can hardly believe his eyes. He thinks he can see trees in the distance. Mr Crackers flies to investigate. Is it possible? Can palm trees grow in the desert? He circles the trees once or twice, and sees a pool of sparkling, blue water. The next moment, he's splashing about in the oasis. "Ooh! That's lovely and cool," he chirrups. Then he flies back to Brian. "There's a place where we can rest," he cries in excitement. "It's only a little way further ahead."

10 August

Just like lemonade

"Is the water safe to drink?" pants Brian, as he collapses under a palm tree. "Yes, I'm sure it is. It's crystal clear," replies Mr Crackers. Brian crawls to the water's edge and begins to drink thirstily. "Mmm!" sighs Brian. "When you're thirsty, water is as tasty as lemonade. Suddenly the two friends hear a loud voice behind them. "Can I help you, gentlemen?" The two friends jump with fright. "Who's that?" whispers Brian nervously.

149

11 August

An alien creature

The voice comes from a bizarre animal standing between two palm trees. Brian and Mr Crackers look round in terror. Brian's mouth drops open in shock. "What's that?" he gasps in horror. Mr Crackers squawks in dismay. "I think it's a monster," he whispers. An alien creature is moving towards them. It has two large humps on its back, and it's even bigger than Brian.

12 August

Brian is speechless

"I see you're strangers here," the alien grunts. Brian is unable to speak and just nods his head. Mr Crackers speaks for him. "Yes we are. This is Brian the bear, and I'm Mr Crackers," he says, pecking Brian sharply on the ear. "Ouch, why did you do that?" Brian shouts. "Because it isn't very polite to stare at strangers," replies Mr Crackers.

13 August

Fatima

"My name is Fatima, and I'm a camel. Sometimes we're called the ships of the desert," smiles the large animal. "Do camels always have humps on their backs?" asks the inquisitive Mr Crackers. "Of course they do," replies the camel. "We use them to store water. There aren't many places to drink in the desert." Brian can't take his eyes off Fatima. "Can we drink some of your water?" he asks. "Of course you can, you foolish bear," laughs Fatima. "Everyone is free to drink as much as they like, here in the desert."

14 August

Couscous

"You must stay here for the night," says Fatima. "I know it's very hot now, but it can get icy cold later." Brian gives her a bewildered stare. "I can't believe it gets cold in the desert," he mutters. Mr Crackers looks rather worried. "We must search for some food. Brian has nothing to eat," he explains to Fatima. "That doesn't matter," she replies cheerily. "Tonight some friends are coming to dinner. We're having couscous, and you're welcome to join us." Fatima gives Brian a curious look. "I'm longing to know what you're doing here. It's not very often we see bears in the desert!"

No place to travel through

The sandy desert is no place
For bears to travel through.
Its burning grains flies in their eyes
And makes their feet ache, too.

Fatima doesn't mind at all,
She has much tougher feet.
And if you've lived there all your life,
You don't care about the heat.

16 August

Mrs Ostrich

Brian goes to rest under a bush. He's exhausted by the heat. What's this? The bush is moving! Brian thinks he's going mad. "Now what? Have I sat on someone's house again?" he groans in panic. Even Mr Crackers looks afraid when he realizes what has happened. Brian has squashed an ostrich. "That's Mrs Ostrich," explains Fatima. "She's terribly shy. She always buries her head in the sand because she thinks no one can see her!"

17 August

Two quarrelsome ladies

"I'm very sorry, I didn't see you standing there," apologizes Brian. "There you are, it works!" exclaims Mrs Ostrich. "He couldn't see me!" she cries, as she flaps her wings in triumph. Fatima shakes her head. "It's not worth trying to answer that," she mutters. Brian and Mr Crackers shrug their shoulders. They don't know how to take these quarrelsome ladies.

18 August

Who's Oscar?

"Have you seen Oscar today?" Fatima asks Mrs Ostrich. She shakes her head. "I haven't seen him yet, but I could look for him," she offers.
"If you see him, tell him not to be late for my party," replies Fatima. "You're right! He isn't the fastest animal around," laughs Mrs Ostrich, as she sticks her head back into the sand.
"Who's Oscar?" asks Mr Crackers.

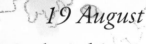

19 August

Only joking?

"Oscar is our little friend, the worm. He tells such funny jokes," explains Fatima. Mr Crackers' eyes begin to shine. "A worm? I love worms. They're delicious!" he says, as his beak waters. Fatima looks at Mr Crackers in horror. "You aren't planning to eat our friend?" she blurts out in horror. "He's only joking, madam," says Brian quickly, nudging Mr Crackers. Mr Crackers looks at him in surprise. "Eh? Oh yes, I was only joking," he chuckles. Fatima takes a deep breath. "Well, I'm glad about that, because I'd hate you to eat a friend of ours," she hisses. "You didn't need to nudge me so hard," Mr Crackers complains to Brian. "It's your own fault!" Brian answers back.

20 August

Nice and juicy

"I can see Oscar," cries Mrs Ostrich. "He's coming out now." Oscar pops his head out of a hole in the sand a moment or two later. "Oops!" he cries in alarm when he sees Mr Crackers. "Who's that bird? He looks very dangerous to me," he mutters. Brian tries to calm him down. "Don't worry! Mr Crackers won't hurt you," he replies gently. "Well, he looked at me as if could eat me raw," says Oscar. "He's right, he looks so nice and juicy," Mr Crackers whispers in Brian's ear. Brian pretends not to hear his friend. "What is couscous?" he asks Fatima, in order to change the subject.

21 August

Terrible thieves

Fatima tells Brian that couscous is made from meat and steamed semolina. Suddenly, they hear nasty laughter. "It's those two again," says Mrs Ostrich. "What's that noise?" asks Brian, pricking up his ears. "That's Trouble and Terror, the hyena brothers," she replies. "They're horrible beasts, I hate them!" Mr Crackers looks scared. "What are they doing here?" he squeaks. "I hope they're not coming to dinner." Fatima looks horrified. "I trust not," she says, "because they're terrible thieves, and they would steal more than the couscous!"

22 August

Trouble and Terror

Two pairs of eyes suddenly gleam behind the bushes. "They're going to have supper soon," whispers Trouble. "It looks like it," replies Terror. "Ssh! there are strangers here." Trouble stares into the sky. "Let's tell the vulture brothers," he whispers quietly. "Aeyee!" he whines, and his eerie tones echo round the desert. Not long afterwards, the hyena brothers hear the sound of flapping wings. "Here come the vultures," whispers Terror, but his eyes are on Mr Crackers. "That bird looks very tasty," he remarks to his brother.

23 August

Brian tells his story

The sun sinks into the horizon as Fatima prepares the meal. Brian tells his story when everyone is sitting round the camp fire, enjoying their couscous. He tells them about Miss Peggy and the wicked witch Endora, about the frog princess and the absent-minded professor. Then he tells them about the circus. How everyone laughs and cheers when they hear what happened to Francisco and Bozo. Fatima, Mrs Ostrich and Oscar listen, without breathing a word, when Brian tells them about Captain Ironhook and his treasure. When Brian has finished his story, everyone begins to talk at once. "What an exciting story," says Oscar. "And what a long way you have come!" cries Mrs Ostrich. "And where are you going to now?" Fatima wants to know.

24 August

The two eavesdroppers

Trouble and Terror have also been listening to Brian's story. "That stupid bear looks rather strong," Trouble whispers to Terror. "Yes, and that little bird looks rather thin," Terror replies. "Shall we go and see what the vultures think?" Trouble suggests. "That's a good idea," says Terror, and the two of them slink away to the dead tree where the vultures are sitting, waiting to see if there will be anything for them to eat.

25 August

Problems?

"That was very nice," Brian murmurs happily, when all the couscous has been eaten up. "But I'm afraid that we might have problems tonight," says Fatima, looking around nervously. "I'm sure that Trouble and Terror are sitting out there watching us, and I heard the vulture brothers flying past just now."
"Was that the two big birds on the dead tree?" asks Mr Crackers. "You must have good eyesight," says Fatima in surprise.
"If those two are nearby, I'm going home," says Oscar and he disappears under the ground. Mrs Ostrich buries her head in the sand in fright.

26 August

Brian keeps watch

"I think I'll just go for a walk and see what those two rascals are up to," says Brian.
"I wouldn't do that if I were you," says Fatima alarmed. "Those two are really dangerous!" But Brian has already got up and is walking in the direction of the bushes where Trouble and Terror are hiding, and having their chat with the vulture brothers. It's quite dark now, and Brian can only see their shining eyes. "Are you always such a nuisance?" he asks. But Trouble and Terror say nothing. They just open their mouths so that Brian can see their sharp teeth.
Brian doesn't feel quite so brave any more.

158

27 August

Brian is very brave

Everything is deathly silent in the oasis. Everyone is holding his breath. Even Trouble and Terror keep perfectly still. They have never known anything like this before. Normally all the animals they meet are afraid of them; but now this stranger has come and doesn't seem to be frightened at all. And he looks very strong! "Well," says Brian, taking a couple of steps forwards. "What are you hanging around for?" Now Trouble and Terror feel rather frightened, and even the vulture brothers begin to move nervously up and down their branches.

28 August

Cowards

When there is still no movement in the bushes, Brian bravely moves forwards another two or three steps. Suddenly he makes a nasty face, lifts his huge claws into the air and growls as loudly as he can: "Grrrrrrrrr!" Terror cries out in fright, and runs off with his tails between his legs.
When Trouble realizes that he is alone with Brian, his last bit of courage vanishes and he quickly runs off after his brother. The vulture brothers, who dare not do anything without the hyena brothers, fly off. "Cowards," growls Brian, as he returns to the camp fire.

29 August

They don't need to know

Fatima, who has stood up to watch Brian's brave deeds from the camp fire, now taps Mrs Ostrich. Slowly Mrs Ostrich lifts her head from the sand "Brian has chased them all away!" Fatima cries in delight. "It can't be true!" exclaims Mrs Ostrich, looking all around nervously. Mr Crackers flies onto Brian's shoulder as his friend proudly approaches the camp fire. "What cowards they all are," says Brian as he sits down again. He decides not to tell them how frightened he felt.

30 August

Fine weather again

Brian is woken by the sun shining down onto his face. Fatima is already busy preparing breakfast and Mr Crackers is keeping her company. Mrs Ostrich also waddles over. "Good morning, Brian" says Fatima cheerily, when she sees he is awake. "Breakfast is almost ready, and it's another fine day." "Doesn't it ever rain here?" asks Mr Crackers. "No, hardly ever," Fatima replies. "But sometimes there's a sandstorm, and then you can't even see your hand in front of your face. But today it's going to stay fine ... I can feel it in my bones."

31 August

On the way to the forest

"How long will it take us to get out of the desert?" Brian asks. "If you're quick, you could reach the forest by afternoon," replies Fatima. Mrs Ostrich gives Brian a hug. "I've made these cakes for you, and packed a bottle of water for your journey. Be sure to stop and see us again. It's so nice to have strong friends like you." Brian beams with pleasure, and Mr Crackers sits proudly on his shoulder. Watched by Fatima and Mrs Ostrich, they set off on their journey. A little further on Oscar sticks his head out of the sand. "Good-bye Brian, good-bye Mr Crackers. Have a good journey and see you again."

1 September

The forest

"I've never seen a forest like this," cries the astonished Brian, when the two friends have finally crossed the desert. "Look at those enormous trees! And look at all those flowers and creepers!" The forest is alive with the sound of birds.

They are chirping, squawking, and chattering to each other. "*I've* never seen so much hustle and bustle," says Mr Crackers in surprise. "Look at the strange creatures swinging from those branches. Do they live in the trees like birds?"

2 September

What a bustle

What a forest meets their eyes,
Trees and plants of every size.
Creepers hang from every bough,
Brian thinks he's dreaming now.
What a bustle, to and fro.
Who lives here? I want to know.

162

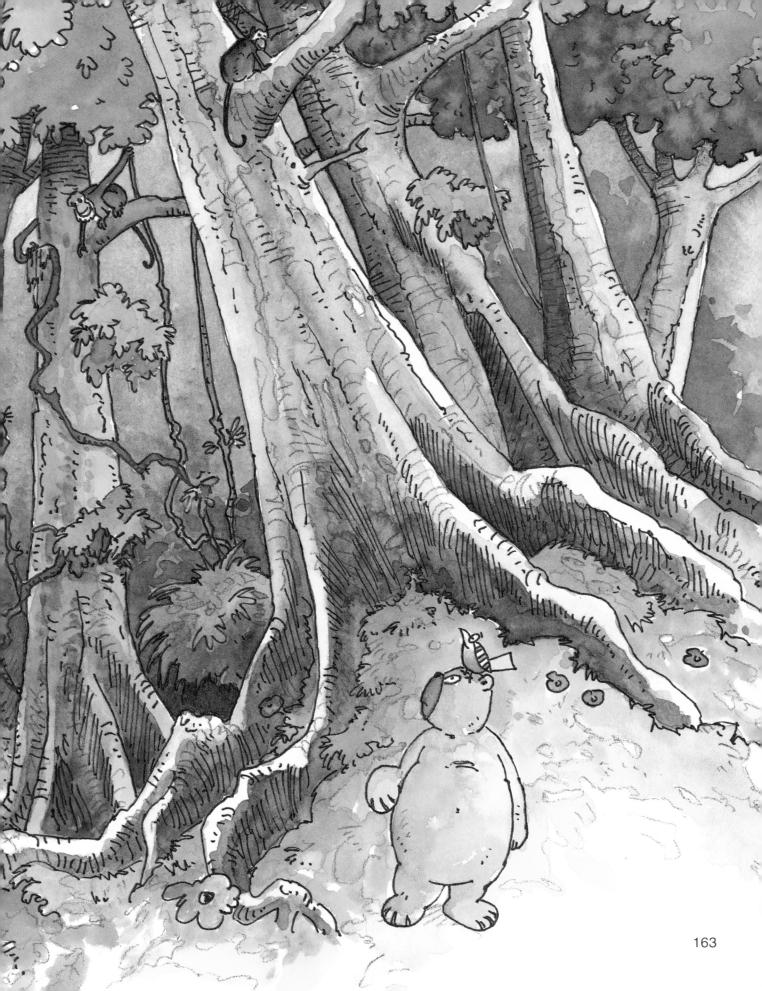

3 September

Mona the monkey

One of the tree creatures catches Brian's eye. "Where did you learn to climb like that?" asks Brian. "I've never seen anything like it!" The tree creature shrugs its shoulders. "I'm a monkey, you silly bear. Monkeys are champion climbers!" Brian looks surprised. "A monkey?" he repeats. "Yes, a monkey! My name's Mona." Mona looks at the chubby bear. "I don't suppose you can climb trees like me?" she teases.
"Oh yes I can," cheeky Brian replies. "I bet you've never seen a climbing bear!"

4 September

Just you wait, you snivelling monkey

Suddenly, Brian spots lots more monkeys peeping down at him from the trees, but he pretends not to notice. "I'll show them what a bear can do," he growls, as he walks over to the tallest tree. "Mind how you go," warns Mr Crackers. Brian mutters something under his breath, and slowly begins his climb. "Come on, fatty!" cries Mona rudely. "Just one more heave and you'll make it." Brian feels very cross indeed. "Fat! I'm not fat," he fumes. "Just you wait, you snivelling monkey!"

164

5 September

Mona's family

"He looks just like poor old Katie," giggles one of the monkeys. "Are you laughing at *me*?" Brian seethes. He's feeling very angry. "No," replies Mona, soothingly. "You climb very well for a bear." Brian has now reached the branch where the monkeys are sitting. "Is this your family?" he asks Mona. "Yes, we're all related," she replies. "This is my brother, Slinger. And that's my cousin, Flicker," says Mona, pointing to a sleepy monkey.

6 September

Katie the cockatoo

Mr Crackers can't stop laughing. Brian looks so funny sitting in a tree. More and more monkeys are arriving to catch a glimpse of the bear. They chatter noisily among themselves, as they swing among the trees. Suddenly, a plump white bird perches beside Mr Crackers. "Hello," says the bird. "My name's Katie, and I'm a cockatoo."

165

7 September

Katie is at it again

Katie stares at Brian. "Who's that great big bear?" she asks Mr Crackers. "That's my friend Brian," he replies. "I think I'll go and take a closer look," says Katie. She flies over to Brian, and perches on a branch close beside him. Now Katie is rather plump, and the branch is rather spindly. Crack! The branch snaps under Katie's weight, and she tumbles towards the ground. Luckily she grabs hold of a twig with her beak, and stops herself falling. The monkeys roll about with laughter. "Poor old Katie is at it again!" they chuckle.

8 September

Sniggering monkey

Katie clambers back beside Brian. "Go on, laugh if you must, you silly monkeys!" she grumbles. Slinger almost falls off his branch. "It could only happen to you," he sniggers. "As soon as you sit on a branch, it snaps. Poor old Katie!" And he begins to roll about laughing. Katie looks the other way. She's very upset by his rudeness. "That hateful monkey," she says.

9 September

A party in the trees

Flicker comes and sits beside Brian. "We're having a party tonight," he says. "You've arrived just in time!" Brian's eyes shine with excitement. "Hooray, a party! What fun!" he cries happily. "You're thinking about the food as usual," remarks the saucy Mr Crackers "It's going to be really special," adds Flicker. "We're going to have some dancing." Brian looks surprised. "Dancing? Up here in the tree? You must be joking!"

10 September

Cheep chirrup, cheep chirrup!

The monkeys are kept very busy preparing for their party. Hundreds of fireflies settle among the leaves to take care of the lighting. Little birds are sitting in rows, practising their songs. "Cheep chirrup, cheep chirrup," they sing. Even the monkeys stop and listen to the melodies. "What a beautiful sound," they whisper. Someone gives Brian a banana. He doesn't know you must peel bananas, so he starts to eat it whole. "Hang on for a minute," cries Mona. "Bananas taste so much better when they're peeled."

11 September

Boa

The monkeys are having tremendous fun as they dance and sing. Even Katie is enjoying herself, waltzing with Slinger. "Poor old Slinger," she says as she steps on his toes. "It could only happen to you!" Suddenly, Brian hears a hissing voice behind his back. "Hello, my name's Boa." Brian turns round and gets the shock of his life. He's never seen such a giant snake before. It's a monster. Mr Crackers is nervous of snakes, so he quickly moves away. But luckily Boa is in a happy mood, like everyone else at the party.

168

12 September

Lazy Paddy

Paddy the panther is dozing peacefully on a nearby branch. Brian goes to say hello. He thinks you should be polite to panthers. Paddy opens his eyes slowly, and looks at Brian with a puzzled frown. "Nice party, isn't it?" begins the bear. "Mmmm," replies the panther. "Are you enjoying the music?" Brian tries again. "I'm a bit lazy today," replies Paddy. "How can you be so sleepy when there's a party going on?" asks Brian in amazement. "I don't like parties, and I've eaten a lot ," replies Paddy the panther, as he closes his eyes again.

13 September

Broken bones?

The animals are having a splendid time at the party. Boa is swaying to the music while Paddy beats time with his tail. Suddenly there's a ghastly screech.
"Oh no," cries Mona. "Come quickly! Poor old Katie has fallen off her perch again." Slinger leaps from branch to branch down the tree. "I hope she hasn't broken anything," he cries in alarm. Brian watches all this activity from the safety of his branch. "Katie should be more careful at her age," he says to Mr Crackers.

169

14 September

A grand old girl

Slinger carefully carries Katie back to her branch. Everyone is asking what happened. Did the branch snap again? "No," says Katie. "I missed my step in the dance, and toppled over!" Brian is feeling smug. He would never make a mistake like that. "You poor old thing," he says in a snooty voice. "She's a grand old girl," interrupts Slinger angrily. "You mustn't call her a poor old thing." Brian blushes with shame. "I shouldn't have said that," he apologizes.

15 September

What a party

What a party,
What a feast.
Lots of fun
For bird and beast.

Hear them singing.
See them clap.
Their feet mark time,
Their bright wings flap.

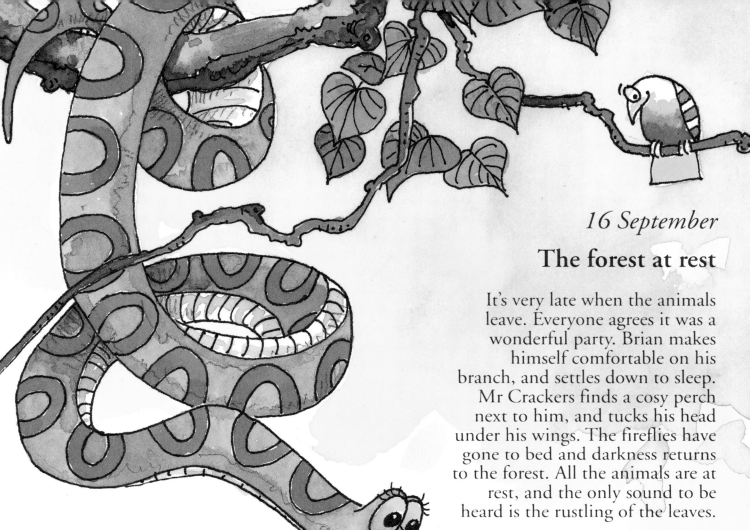

16 September

The forest at rest

It's very late when the animals leave. Everyone agrees it was a wonderful party. Brian makes himself comfortable on his branch, and settles down to sleep. Mr Crackers finds a cosy perch next to him, and tucks his head under his wings. The fireflies have gone to bed and darkness returns to the forest. All the animals are at rest, and the only sound to be heard is the rustling of the leaves.

17 September

Boa can read minds

Brian is woken by a spitting noise the following morning. When he opens his eyes, he sees Boa's face swaying just above him. "Good morning, Brian," the snake hisses. "Did you sleep well?" Brian feels rather dazed. "Yes, thank you," he mumbles. It's not every morning that Brian is woken by a snake swinging in front of his nose. He looks around for his friend. "Where's Mr Crackers?" he asks nervously. Boa looks deep into Brian's eyes. "I don't eat friends," he hisses in his menacing voice. "How did you know what I was thinking?" Brian asks in surprise. "It's not very difficult with bears like you," laughs Boa, as he slithers away. "Good-bye, Brian."

171

18 September

Mira the giraffe

Brian is sitting with Mr Crackers, enjoying a lovely breakfast of bananas. Suddenly, a face appears beside his branch. Mr Crackers is so frightened, he drops his banana. Brian stares at the face with its soft brown eyes, and watches as its tongue darts out of its mouth to nibble at leaves. His gaze shifts, and he looks down to the ground.

"Thank goodness," he sighs, as he realizes the head is attached to a very long neck. "I thought I was dreaming." The face starts to smile. "Hello, strangers," says a soft voice. "It's only me. I'm Mira the giraffe!"

19 September

Head in the clouds

Brian recovers from his amazement. "Why didn't we see you at the party last night?" he asks Mira. "I was walking around with my head in the clouds, and forgot the time," explains the giraffe. "What about *you*? Did you come to the forest specially for the party?" Brian takes a bite from his banana. "No," he replies. "We came here by chance." And once again, he tells his story. When he finishes, Brian hears loud applause. All the animals have come to listen, and they really enjoyed his adventures.

172

20 September

Riding on Mira's back

"Perhaps I can help you on your way," offers Mira. "You can ride on my back as far as the river." Mr Crackers thinks it's a wonderful idea. "Yippee!" he exclaims. "That would be so exciting." Brian looks doubtful. "I might be too heavy for you," he says sadly. "Don't worry," Mira replies. "That lazy panther often rides on my back, so I'm used to heavyweights!"

173

21 September

Like a slide

Brian is thrilled by Mira's idea. With the help of the giraffe's long legs, they'll travel much faster. Brian looks down from his tree. "How will I get onto your back?" he asks Mira. "Watch the children," replies Mona. "All our youngsters slide down her neck, so why don't you try it?" "Mmmm! That sounds interesting," replies Brian carefully. "Go on, have a go!" the monkeys urge Brian. And, to their great delight, he clambers from his branch and slides down Mira's neck.

22 September

On the way to the river

Mira lopes through the forest on her long spindly legs. She stops now and then to pluck a few tender shoots, then continues on her way. She tells Brian all about life in the forest. And then she describes the river. "Most of us go there to drink," she says. "And the elephants come to bathe." Elephants! Brian remembers the circus and shivers. "We know all about elephants," he says, as he bounces up and down on Mira's back. He has to cling onto Mira's neck to stop himself from falling.

23 September

A lone tree

A vast expanse of grassland greets them as they leave the forest. "Now I can use my legs properly," cries Mira. "Hold tight, Brian!" And she stretches her legs and gallops across the plain. Brian clings on for dear life, and closes his eyes in fright. Meanwhile, Mr Crackers has flown on ahead with Katie. Suddenly, Katie gives a loud squawk. "Hey, Mr Crackers! Why don't we stop for a rest?" And without waiting for a reply, she flies towards a shady tree.

24 September

Grizzle's tree

Katie makes a clumsy landing on the topmost branch of the tree. Mr Crackers flutters around to help her. He doesn't want Katie toppling over! "Well, that was a long flight," sighs Katie. "I think we've still got some way to go," says Mr Crackers. "Can you manage it? I don't think you were meant for long distance flying." Katie clambers down onto another branch. "No, I certainly wasn't," she says. "By the way, this is Grizzle's tree." Mr Crackers looks around him. "Who's Grizzle?" he asks. "Grizzle is a very friendly bat," replies Katie.

25 September

Grizzle can't sleep

"Hello, Katie," says a voice, from somewhere deep in the tree. "I haven't seen you for a long time. Where have you been?" Mr Crackers tracks the voice, and spots the bat hanging upside down from a twig, shaded by the leaves. "Did we wake you up?" Katie asks Grizzle. "No," he replies. "I've been awake for a long time. I just can't get to sleep." Katie has a bright idea. "Perhaps it's because you sleep upside down. You should try sleeping the right way up, like everyone else," she suggests. "Have you ever seen a bat sleeping the right way up?" grumbles Grizzle. Katie ruffles her feathers. "*I* couldn't sleep upside down," she says. "But you're not a bat, you silly bird," interrupts Mr Crackers.

26 September

Everyone talks at once

Brian and Mira have arrived at Grizzle's tree. Mira thrusts her head among the leaves. "Is everything all right?" she asks. "I suppose it is," grumbles Grizzle. He's still a bit annoyed with Katie, and is longing to get some sleep. "What's going on?" asks Brian, as he pokes his head through the leaves. "Grizzle can't get to sleep," replies Mr Crackers. Everyone begins to talk at once. They've all got advice for Grizzle.

27 September

Katie plays a trick

Katie and Mr Crackers both decide to ride on Mira's back for the last part of the journey. The four friends wish Grizzle a good day's sleep before they set out for the river. Katie soon gets bored with riding on Mira's back, and decides to play a trick. She hops onto Mira's head and then slides down her neck, landing with a bump against Brian's tummy. "I think you must have learnt that trick from the monkeys," chuckles Mira.

177

28 September

A moving stone

It isn't long before the four friends reach the river. Brian is glad to slither off Mira's back because he has such a sore bottom! The river looks very inviting. "I think I'll go and have a dip," says Brian. "There's so much dust in my fur." There are lots of large boulders lining the river bank, and Brian hops from one to the other. But what's happening? One of the boulders has started to move just as Brian steps onto it.

29 September

Brian gets a ducking

"Hey, what's going on? Do you always trample on people's backs without asking permission?" grouches a deep voice from the river. Brian peers down at the boulder, and realizes he's standing on a huge animal. "I beg your pardon, I thought you were a stepping stone," he splutters, taking a pace backwards. Splash! Brian lands in the river beside a giant hippopotamus, and gets an unexpected ducking.

30 September

Even Brian has a chuckle

Brian comes to the surface, spluttering and choking. Mira and Katie start to giggle. Mr Crackers joins in and soon there's an explosion of laughter. Mira's knees wobble while she guffaws. Katie thinks it's so funny, she's rolling about with laughter. Then she rolls once too often and falls into the river. "Help! I can't swim," she cries. "I'm drowning!" Brian fishes her out. When he sees the poor old bird standing dripping on the river bank, it's Brian's turn to chuckle.

1 October

Water, water

Water for bathing
And water for drinking.
Watch out for stepping stones,
Or you may end up sinking.

Are you sure it's a rock?
Or is it a hippo?
If you're not careful,
You may take a dip, oh!

2 October

A jolly crowd

It's very crowded on the river bank. All sorts of
animals have come down to drink. Brian and
Mr Crackers make lots of new friends.
There's Hippo the hippopotamus, Tom and Pete
the elephant twins, Harry the thrush, and
Ronnie the rhinoceros. They are a jolly crowd.
Hippo chats to Ronnie, Mira gossips with Tom
and Pete, and Brian listens to the cheerful song
of Harry the thrush. Katie tries to join in, but
she has a terrible voice.

3 October

Hunters nearby

Brian tells Ronnie they are journeying west. "You'd better watch out for hunters!" warns the rhino. "Hunters?" exclaims Brian in alarm. "Who are they hunting?" He remembers the time hunters trailed him, and Mr Crackers came to the rescue. "They've been after me, and Tom and Pete," says Ronnie. "With guns," adds Pete. "They've been shooting at us," declares Tom indignantly. "Why do they do it?" asks Brian angrily. "It's not a friendly thing to do. They might hit you! We must do something about it!"

4 October

Ronnie has a bright idea

"We should get our own back on the hunters," declares Mr Crackers. "They should know how it feels to be hunted!" Everyone snorts their approval, but how can they do it? Ronnie has a bright idea. "There's an underground cave over there. Why don't we cover the entrance and trick the hunters. We can trap them if they fall into the cave!" Everyone thinks this is a terrific idea, and Harry the thrush makes up a song about it.

5 October

Harry's song

Those beastly hunters with their guns
Make forest life a bore.
To let them know just how it feels,
We've planned a nasty fall.

So watch out, hunters. Watch your steps.
You're wrong to think we're dumb.
A clever trap is planned for you,
Beware! For here we come.

6 October

The trap is set

Everyone gets to work with a will. Mira snaps branches from the trees. Tom and Pete gather them in their trunks and carry them to the cave. Then Ronnie, Hippo, and Brian carefully arrange them over the entrance. At last the trap is ready. "Yippee!" cries Brian. "Now it's time for the hunters!" Mr Crackers looks thoughtful. "Who's going to lure the hunters in this direction?" he asks. "Why don't we do it?" suggests Tom. Pete isn't sure this is a good idea, but in the end he agrees to it. Together, the elephant twins set off in search of the hunters.

7 October

Skinny and Baldy

The two hunters have pitched their camp on the river bank, not far from Brian and his friends. One is scrawny and thin, the other is bald and fat. Skinny is cleaning his gun, and Baldy is looking out across the river. "We almost winged one of those elephants," mutters Baldy. "But you're a useless shot, Skinny. You always miss." Skinny looks cross. "Well, you're not much better yourself!" he grumbles. Everything looks peaceful along the river bank. Skinny and Baldy have no idea what's waiting for them round the corner!

8 October

Charge!

Tom lifts his trunk into the air. "I can smell them," he whispers. "They're pitched their tent by the river." Pete is first to spot the hunters' camp. Skinny and Baldy are sitting on the river bank, with their backs to each other. "Now!" trumpets Tom, as he starts to charge. "Gotcha!" trumpets Pete, as he knocks their tent over. Skinny and Baldy cry out in horror. "I told you not to pitch the tent there," cries Skinny. "It's your fault," cries Baldy.

185

9 October

After them!

"What are we going to do?" whines Skinny. "Those elephants have destroyed our tent and we can't sleep out in the open." Baldy looks furious. "Don't just stand there! Do something! Get your gun!" But Tom and Pete have disappeared into the trees. "After them!" cries Baldy, snatching up his gun. Katie and Mr Crackers are perched in a tree close to the hunters' camp. They watch the elephants disappear into the trees. "Now it's our turn!" whispers Mr Crackers.

10 October

Under attack!

Mr Crackers swoops down, followed by Katie. They zoom over the heads of Skinny and Baldy and peck at them. "Ouch! That hurt," wails Skinny. "After them!" cries Baldy. "They're attacking us!" shrieks Skinny. Baldy is made of sterner stuff. "I'll get you for that!" he roars, shaking his fist at Katie and Mr Crackers. Then he chases after the birds like a mad man.

11 October

An end to your mischief

Mr Crackers and Katie swoop over the entrance to the underground cave. Skinny and Baldy charge after them. Neither of them look where they're putting their feet. "Crack!" go the branches as they snap under the men's weight. "Aaargh!" cry the hunters as they fall into the cave. All the animals stand round the edge of the cave, staring at Skinny and Baldy. Brian picks up their guns and throws them into the river. "There," he growls. "Now that's an end to your mischief."

12 October

A taste of your own medicine

"We promise not to hunt you any more," grovels Skinny. He knows he's trapped in the cave and can't escape. He needs the animals' help. "Why did you do this to us?" moans Baldy. Brian looks very stern. "So you know what it's like to be hunted," he replies grimly. "I've thrown your guns away, so you're at our mercy!" Tom raises his trunk in triumph. "Now you're getting a taste of your own medicine!" he trumpets. Pete starts to laugh, and everyone joins in.

13 October

Building a raft

After a while, peace returns to the river bank. The animals have let Skinny and Baldy go after they promised to give up hunting. Now the animals are discussing the quickest way for Brian and Mr Crackers to reach Wizard Gombal. Ronnie hasn't said anything for a long time. "I know! We could build a raft," the rhino exclaims. "Then we could ask Lizzy the crocodile to tow it to Wizard Gombal's castle." Pete starts searching for logs. "What a whizzo idea!" he cries. "Leave it to me! I know just what we need to build a raft."

14 October

Lizzy

When the raft is built, Hippo swims off to find Lizzy. "Here she is, at last!" laughs Hippo, introducing a giant crocodile to Brian and Mr Crackers. "She looks ever so fierce," whispers Mr Crackers in Brian's ear. "Well, that's what people say about bears, but *I'm* very friendly," replies Brian. "Don't worry! I'll take you to the Great Sea where the Wizard lives," says Lizzy. She's a nice crocodile. She doesn't want to scare Mr Crackers.

15 October

On the raft

The animals wave goodbye as Brian and Mr Crackers swing out into the river on their raft, ready to start their journey. "What a pity they have to go," sighs Katie. "Yes," replies Mira. "What fun we had, and what adventures!" Katie climbs up Mira's neck and clings on waving her wing until Brian and Mr Crackers disappear round a bend in the river.

16 October

What a different story

Carried by a tall giraffe,
Brian could see for ever.
What a different story now,
On a raft, in the river.

Keep your feet tucked in, my friend,
Or they'll get cold and wet.
Keep quite still! Don't tilt the raft!
Lizzy hasn't finished yet.

17 October

All those teeth

The raft moves swiftly through the water, towed by
the faithful Lizzy. "My, you can certainly move!" gasps Brian,
when the crocodile looks round to see if everything's all right.
Lizzy laughs out loud and shows her fearful teeth. Mr Crackers
is shocked to see how many she has. He's frightened by her teeth,
and moves closer to Brian.

18 October

Is Lizzy hungry?

"Are you always so quiet?" Lizzy asks. "Or don't you like rafting?" Brian and Mr Crackers have hardly exchanged a word since they started their journey. "We're loving it," replies Brian. "But there's so much to see along the bank, and I've been watching the fish in the river." Lizzy sighs. "The fish are lucky I can't let go of this raft. Otherwise I'd gobble them up for my dinner!" Mr Crackers turns pale. "Are you hungry?" he asks in a small voice. "No," replies Lizzy. "But if a fish is stupid enough to swim into my mouth, I'd grab it!"

19 October

Lizzy's family

Brian and Mr Crackers are quietly eating the bananas they brought with them from the forest. "Look, that's where I live," Lizzy shouts. "And there are my brothers and sisters. Let's go and say hello," she cries, thrashing her tail from side to side to attract their attention. "Hey, mind what you're doing," warns Brian, as the water splashes his fur. "I've had a bath this week, and that's enough for a bear," he grumbles. "Don't get cross," says Lizzy, blushing. "I forgot I was towing a raft. I'm sorry!"

191

20 October

Where's the castle

The river widens as it flows into the ocean. "Look over there!" cries Lizzy. "You can see Wizard Gombal's castle." Brian jerks awake. He has been lulled into a doze by the gentle movement of the raft. "What? Where?" he cries, as he searches the horizon. Brian can't see anything. Thin bands of mist hang above the ocean. Mr Crackers appears out of the mist, and lands on Brian's shoulder. "We're nearly there now. I've just been over to investigate," he tells Brian. "It's a fantastic place, built on a rock," he explains, pointing to the castle.

Another elf, called Cobweb

The mist is still hanging over the ocean when the three friends draw level with the steps leading up to the castle. "Good morning, Lizzy," says a cheerful voice. "I see you've brought some guests with you." Brian looks around in surprise, and sees a little man with very much wings who reminds him of Mustardseed. "I'm Cobweb, and I'm an elf," says the little man. "It's my job to greet Wizard Gombal's guests. I bid you welcome to his castle." The elf gives a graceful bow. "That will do, Cobweb," says a deep voice. "Our guests are tired and need to rest." It's the voice of Wizard Gombal.

22 October

Silly Cobweb

"Show our guests to their rooms, Cobweb, and offer them some refreshment," requests the Wizard. "Give them what, sir?" asks Cobweb, looking confused. "Something to eat, numskull," booms Wizard Gombal. "Oh dear! I'm being stupid again," wails the elf. "I think I'll fly away as fast as I can, before the wizard gets cross with me." "Hey," cries Brian. "Not so fast! Remember we're tired and hungry." Cobweb bursts into tears. "I'm only trying to do my best. Don't get angry with me." Mr Crackers feels sorry for the elf. "Oh dear, you *are* in a state," he says. "You're just like the rest," howls Cobweb. "Everyone hates me!"

193

23 October

The never-ending staircase

Brian and Mr Crackers thank Lizzy for towing their raft, and climb up the steps to the castle. "Is it much further to our room?" pants Brian. "No, it's just up there," replies Cobweb, pointing to a spiral staircase. "It looks like a never-ending staircase to me," sighs Brian. "Where does it go to?" asks Mr Crackers. "To the tower room," replies Cobweb. "It has the best view in the castle." Brian yawns. "That sounds lovely, but I'm ever so tired," he murmurs. "It has the softest bed in the castle," Cobweb tells the bear. "But if you hang around, you'll never get there!" Brian pants for breath as he begins the long climb to his bedroom.

24 October

Be careful, Brian!

"This is the great dream-bed," announces Cobweb, pointing to a large four-poster. "Whoever sleeps in this bed has the loveliest dreams you can ever imagine." Brian grunts huffily. "I *always* have nice dreams, whatever bed I sleep in," he says in a sleepy growl. "But it does look lovely and soft," he remarks, as he bounces onto the bed. "Look out!" cries Cobweb. "Mind you don't break the bed, you silly bear. It's built for sleeping, not bouncing!" and muttering to himself, he leaves the room. "I didn't do anything wrong, did I?" Brian asks Mr Crackers. His friend tucks his wings against his body and yawns. "Let's go to sleep, I'm exhausted!"

25 October

What haste!

The next morning, Brian wakes up feeling ever so bright and chipper. There's a knock on the door while he's having a stretch. "Hello, did you sleep well?" Cobweb's voice inquires. "Breakfast is ready." Brian bounds to his feet. "Let's go down at once," he cries eagerly, pushing open the door. He almost knocks Cobweb over in his haste, he's so anxious for his breakfast.

Wizard Gombal is waiting for them downstairs. "Good morning, my friends. I've prepared a lovely breakfast," he greets Brian and Mr Crackers. The table is heavily laden with delicious things to eat. Brian looks hungrily at all the food, but he can't see any honey. Wizard Gombal notices the disappointment on his face. "Of course, how silly of me. I've forgotten the honey!" He waves his wand and a huge pot of honey appears, right under Brian's nose.

I can always magic another pot

Brian stares at the honey pot in surprise. He picks it up carefully, and takes a pawful of honey. "Mmmm! It's delicious! I wish I had a magic wand. I would never have to climb a tree again to search for honey!" Mr Crackers smiles. "And you wouldn't fall out, either," he murmurs. Brian's paw goes back to the pot. "Hang on a minute, we haven't started breakfast yet!" blurts out Mr Crackers. "You're gobbling up the honey. It isn't very polite, you know." Brian's face reddens. "Oh, I'm sorry," he says, putting the honey pot back on the table. "Don't worry," laughs the Wizard. "I can always magic another pot." Brian stares at the Wizard in disbelief. "You're sure?" he asks, as he takes another pawful.

27 October

These dragons breathe fire

"Now then, let me see. The fourth door! Magic pondweed, eh? No, that won't be easy, not easy at all," mutters Wizard Gombal. "Why is it so difficult?" asks Mr Crackers. "If you want to reach the fourth door, you must pass through Dragon Valley," replies the Wizard. Brian looks alarmed. "That sounds rather frightening!" he exclaims, with his mouth full of honey. "Are the dragons dangerous?" Mr Crackers asks. "Yes, you must be very careful. These dragons breathe fire," replies Wizard Gombal. "They are very big and ugly, too," adds Cobweb.

28 October

Where's the frog princess?

Everyone is in the tower room, standing at the window. Wizard Gombal points to the mountains, glimmering blue in the distance. "Dragon Valley is beyond those mountains," says the Wizard. Brian's thoughts are on other things. "What must we do when we've *found* the pondweed?" he asks. "Well, the pondweed has great magical powers. If you hold it in your hand, you'll be able to pass through the fourth door and return to your own country." Brian looks puzzled. "But we've got to find the frog princess. We can't go back without her." Mr Crackers nods in agreement. "But we don't know where she is," he says, looking hopefully at Wizard Gombal.

29 October

Another tele-mirror?

Wizard Gombal strokes his beard. "We must go down to my laboratory. I must look into my crystal ball to see if I can find the frog princess." Brian is riveted. "Is it like Professor Warbler's tele-mirror?" he asks. Wizard Gombal lifts his nose in the air. "I don't have anything to do with such newfangled inventions. I much prefer the old-fashioned crystal ball, like the one my grandfather used," he says snootily. "Isn't this exciting!" exclaims Brian, as he follows the Wizard and Cobweb down the stairs to the laboratory.

30 October

How old is the Wizard?

"My laboratory is down in the cellar," explains the Wizard, after Brian has complained at the number of stairs. "I don't come down here very often, now. I used to, of course, when I was working on my spells." Mr Crackers glances at the cobwebs hanging from the ceiling, and the dust coating the stairs. "When was that? A hundred years ago?" he jokes. Cobweb laughs. "More like one hundred and fifty years ago!" he says. "Did you know the Wizard is at least two hundred years old!" Mr Crackers can't believe his ears. "But that's impossible!" he cries. Cobweb shrugs his shoulders. "Well, it's the truth," he replies.

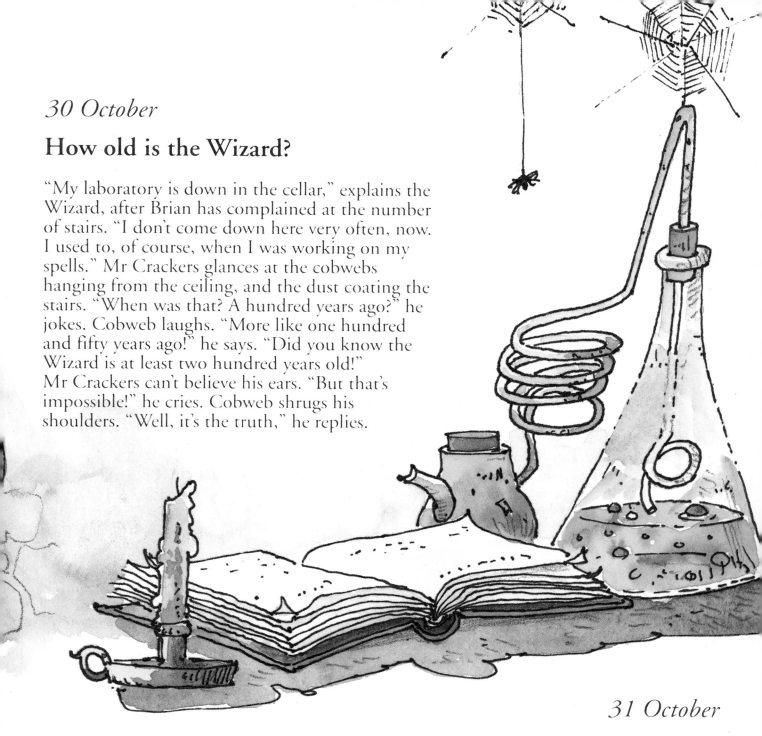

31 October

In the cellar

"You'd better light some candles," the Wizard tells Cobweb, when everyone's in the cellar. "I'm afraid I've forgotten the spell!" Brian and Mr Crackers glance around the laboratory. "Ugh! It's spooky," shivers Mr Crackers, ruffling his feathers. "Look at those spiders!" shudders Brian the bear. A thick layer of dust covers the Wizard's cellar, and there are great black cobwebs hanging everywhere. "Cobweb! Remind me when you last cleaned my laboratory?" asks Wizard Gombal. The elf doesn't reply. If there is one job Cobweb hates, it's cleaning cellars!

1 November

The crystal ball

"Eureka!" cries the Wizard. "Here's my crystal ball!" And he blows a huge cloud of dust from the table. Brian's nose starts to twitch. "Atishoo! Atishoo-oo!" he sneezes. "Come, my friends," says the Wizard. "Let's see if we can find the frog princess." He sweeps his sleeve over the crystal ball, and it begins to hum gently. Brian watches anxiously as the Wizard chants a magic spell. Suddenly a little frog appears in the crystal. "Is that the princess?" asks Brian. "Well I never!" exclaims Mr Crackers.

2 November

East, west, home's best

Little princess, little frog,
At last we've found you, through the fog.
Brian gives a hearty cheer,
Now we can all go home from here.

Though adventures can be fun,
Brian hopes they'll soon be done.
"East, west, home's best!" is what we say,
Time for us to go home and stay!

200

3 November

Cheeky Cobweb

Everyone stares at the crystal ball. "It's the frog princess!" exclaims Mr Crackers. "Where is she?" asks Brian. "Be patient, my friends. We'll know soon enough!" replies the Wizard, as he wipes the remaining dust from the crystal ball. "Good! Now we can see her clearly." After a short while, he looks at Cobweb. "Do you know this place?" he asks the elf. Cobweb is hovering close to Brian's ear. "I thought he would never ask," he whispers. "Don't be cheeky," interrupts the Wizard in a stern voice. "Tell us exactly what you know."

4 November

Not those dragons again!

"The princess is trapped in a pool of water," says Cobweb. "That's obvious!" growls Brian. "Judging from the colour of the water," continues Cobweb. "I think she's caught in the Dragon's Pool." Brian looks uneasy. "Not those dragons again!" he groans. "As far as I know, there's only *one* dragon in the valley," says Cobweb. "But he's a very nasty dragon. When he's angry, he hisses fire." The elf gives Brian a troubled look. "I'm glad *I* don't have to rescue the princess," he murmurs.

5 November

Is Brian afraid?

"I'm not afraid of dragons, if that's what you're thinking," says Brian bravely, looking Cobweb straight in the eye. Mr Crackers is perching on his friend's shoulder. "Well, *I'm* rather frightened, you know," he whispers in Brian's ear. "That's only to be expected," says Brian. "You're a bird, but *I'm* a bear!" Mr Crackers isn't fooled by Brian's brave words. He sees Brian gulp and feels him tremble. Meanwhile, the Wizard is searching through a cupboard. "It must be here somewhere," he murmurs. "Aha, here it is!" he exclaims in triumph, as he puts a small casket on the table.

6 November

Brian is given a magic charm

"This casket contains a magic jewel," the Wizard tells Brian. "As long as you wear it, it will shield you from harm." He places the jewel round Brian's neck. "But what about my friend, Mr Crackers? Doesn't he need a jewel to protect him, too?" asks Brian. "This will shield you both," the Wizard replies. "It will also protect anyone else who needs it on your journey to the fourth door." Cobweb touches the magic jewel. "Is that why you hid it in this casket?" he asks Wizard Gombal. "This is very powerful magic," the Wizard replies firmly. "Of course I kept it hidden from a cheeky elf like you!"

7 November

Mr Crackers scolds Brian

Brian enters the great hall of the castle, wearing his magic jewel. "Wizard Gombal must think a lot of me, to give me this magic jewel!" he proudly declares to Mr Crackers. "Huh! Anyone would think you were the only one who deserves a magic charm," scowls Mr Crackers. "There are lots more animals in danger." Brian doesn't like being scolded by his friend. "You always find something nasty to say," he complains. Then he pauses for a moment. "But I suppose you're right! Every creature should have a magic jewel." Mr Crackers agrees. "It would be marvellous," he says. "No one would be frightened ever again!"

8 November

On the way to the Dragon Valley

At last it's time to leave the castle. "Take care," calls Wizard Gombal. "Good luck with the dragon," shouts Cobweb, as they wave goodbye to their friends. Brian swings his arms as he marches along the mountain path, on his way to Dragon Valley. Mr Crackers hums a tune to keep up his spirits. "I wonder what's going to happen to us next?" Brian asks Mr Crackers. "I do miss our forest. I wish we were home." Mr Crackers nods his head. "Well, we're nearing the end of our journey," he says, trying to cheer his friend. "Shall we sing a song?" Brian is surprised. "But you always say I sing out of tune. Perhaps this magic jewel will improve my voice." And, singing happily, the two friends continue on their way.

9 November

Does the dragon know we're coming?

Brian and Mr Crackers approach Dragon Valley as evening falls. "This is where the dragon lives," says Brian, looking round anxiously. "Do you think he knows we're coming?" whispers Mr Crackers. "I hope not," Brian replies with a shiver. "Otherwise the dragon might be lying in wait, ready to attack us." He looks uncertainly at his friend. "I don't know what I'd do if that happened." Mr Crackers cheeps in fright. "We could run away as fast as we can?" he suggests. "Yes, but then we'd never rescue the frog princess," replies Brian. He straightens his back and walks down the path into Dragon Valley.

205

10 November

Lovely sweet berries

"It's quiet here, isn't it? In fact it's *too* quiet," remarks Mr Crackers. "I think I'll fly on ahead to see if there's any sign of the dragon." Brian thinks this is a splendid idea. He's feeling very hungry, and he's spotted some lovely juicy berries on a bush near the path. "I'll wait here for you," says Brian. Mr Crackers has seen the berries, too. "You certainly recognize good food when you see it," he laughs, as he flies off. Brian tastes one of the berries. "Mmmm! Mmmmmm!" he exclaims with pleasure. "These are simply delicious!"
And he crams his mouth full of berries. So full, in fact, that his whole face is stained red with their juice.

11 November

No sign of the dragon

Mr Crackers returns to find Brian snoozing peacefully on the grass. His tummy looks blown out from eating all those berries. "Did you enjoy your supper?" asks Mr Crackers. Brian sits up with a start, and stares round nervously. "Oh, it's only you!" he sighs with relief. "I thought you were the dragon." Mr Crackers bursts out laughing. "That's one thing you don't have to worry about. I'd be more worried about indigestion!" jokes Mr Crackers. Then he becomes more serious. "I couldn't see a sign of the dragon," continues Mr Crackers. "But there's a cave just up the path. Why don't we sleep there tonight?" Brian hauls himself to his feet. "That's a good idea," he replies. "I am feeling rather tired, and it looks like rain," he replies, looking at the dark clouds gathering on the horizon.

12 November

Nice and warm tonight

Brian peers inside the cave, but it's so dark he can't see a thing. "It's pitch dark in there," he tells Mr Crackers. "Are you afraid of the dark?" asks his friend. "Of course not!" Brian replies, sticking out his chest with a laugh. But to tell you the truth, he is rather frightened. You can shelter in a cave, but you never know who's living there. You might disturb a dragon! Then Brian has an idea. "Let's light a fire. It'll keep us nice and warm tonight," he says to his friend. "And it will give you nightlight," thinks Mr Crackers.

13 November

A lovely comfy bed

Brian gathers armfuls of branches and twigs, and builds them into a bonfire. Then he spots a pile of leaves. "This will make us a comfy bed," he tells his friend. "They're so soft and warm," sighs Mr Crackers, as he sinks into the leaves. Brian decides to take another look around the cave before he settles down to sleep. He examines all the nooks and crannies. "Hey, Mr Crackers! There's something on the ceiling," he whispers to his friend. Mr Crackers looks up. "It's only a spider," he chuckles.

14 November

Who's rude?

"I'm not afraid of spiders," says Brian in his best bear's voice. "But it is rather a big one!" The spider slowly lowers itself on a thread, until it dangles in front of Brian's nose. "What are you doing in *my* cave?" he asks the bear. "I think you should introduce yourself before you ask us questions," interrupts Mr Crackers.
"You aren't very polite, you know," says Brian. "I think you're rude, too. Fancy taking over my house without being invited," grumbles the spider. Brian and Mr Crackers look at him in surprise. "Is this house yours?" asks Mr Crackers. "Yes it is," replies the spider. "I live here with the dragon!"

15 November

The dragon's very ill

"Is this really the dragon's house?" asks Brian in alarm. Mr Crackers turns very pale. "Oh yes it is," replies the spider. "We've lived here for years together." Brian moves towards the entrance of the cave. "I think we'd better go," says Brian. "We don't want to be a nuisance," adds Mr Crackers. "Please stay for the night, you don't bother me," pleads the spider. Brian tries to think of an excuse to leave. "I've been very lonely here recently," continues the spider. "The dragon is so ill, he can't leave his bed. I would be very glad of your company." Brian sighs with relief. "In that case we'll stay," he says, as he moves back to the fire.

16 November

What's wrong with the dragon?

"What's wrong with the dragon?" asks Brian.
"I'm not sure," replies the spider. "I think he's caught
a bad cold. But whatever it is, he's very unwell," he
continues. "He doesn't look himself, and he can't breathe
fire any more." Mr Crackers' face is slowly returning
to its normal colour. "Where is the dragon?" he wants to
know. "Why, he's here in the cave, of course," replies
the spider. Brian feels a shiver run down his spine.
"Here in *this* cave?" he asks in a squeaky voice.
"Yes, he's in his bedroom at the back of the cave. Why don't
you go in and see him?" asks the spider. Brian doesn't know
what to think. Would a sick dragon welcome visitors?

17 November

A strange thing

In the dragon's deep, dark cave,
Full of shadows, cold and still.
Brian's heart is beating fast,
Is the dragon really ill?

Can he really trust the spider?
Is the spider telling lies?
Brian cannot understand it,
And his mouth is feeling dry.

Overcome by curiosity

"Come on, let's see if the dragon's awake,"
begs the spider. "Oh, I'm not sure about that,"
replies Brian. "Perhaps he's feeling disagreeable,
and I don't want to disturb a disagreeable dragon!"
The spider chuckles. "He's too sick to hurt you,"
he replies. Brian's curiosity gets the better of him.
It's not every day you get the chance to
visit a dragon. He looks at Mr Crackers.
"What do you think, my friend?"
Mr Crackers just shrugs his shoulders,
and doesn't bother to reply.

19 November

A visit to the dragon

Brian and Mr Crackers follow the spider into the dark shadows at the back of the cave. They pass along a tunnel which leads into a lofty, inner chamber. The dragon is lying in a pool of moonlight, shining through a cleft in the roof of the cave. Brian holds his breath as the dragon stirs. "Is that you, spider?" moans the dragon, in a rasping voice "Yes, it's me," replies the spider, with no regard for English grammar. "I've brought some visitors to see you." The dragon tries to lift his head from the floor. "I don't feel like having visitors," he mumbles, and he lets his head fall back to the floor. "He looks in a sorry state," Brian whispers to Mr Crackers.

20 November

The dragon is really unwell

Brian is no longer afraid of the dragon. He takes a couple of steps forward. "What's made you so ill?" he asks quietly. The dragon looks at Brian with his huge sad eyes. "It all began with a cold," he whispers. "Then I couldn't breathe fire any more. Now I'm so weak, I can't even move." Mr Crackers feels very sorry for the dragon. "Can we do anything for you?" he asks. "No, thank you. You won't be able to cure me," replies the dragon sadly, and closes his eyes. Suddenly Brian has a bright idea. What about Wizard Gombal's magic jewel?

Can the magic jewel help?

"Perhaps Wizard Gombal's magic jewel can make the dragon better," exclaims Brian. Mr Crackers looks at him in surprise. "Of course, the magic jewel!" he cries. "Why didn't we think of it before?" The dragon glances at Brian hopefully. "Have you really got a magic charm?" he asks. The spider looks at Brian with a happy smile on his face. "You mean my friend could get better!" he cries, as he swings up and down on his thread with joy. Brian takes the magic jewel from his neck, and hangs it from the dragon's nose. Then he uses his paw to polish the jewel.

22 November

Brian doesn't know any magic spells

Everyone watches eagerly, as the jewel slowly begins to glow. "Perhaps you should chant a magic spell," suggests the spider. "The Wizard didn't say anything about magic spells," murmurs Brian, as he continues to polish the jewel. "Are you feeling any better?" Mr Crackers asks the dragon. The dragon opens his eyes. "No, I don't think it's working," he whispers, and a large tear flows down his cheek. Brian feels mixed up. What else should he do? "Look! Smoke's coming out of the dragon's nostrils!" cries the spider.

23 November

No smoke without fire!

Brian is amazed to see wafts of smoke drifting out of the dragon's nostrils. "Look at this!" he cries. "There's no smoke without fire." The dragon's nose starts to twitch. "A ...a ... atishoo!" he sneezes, and a great flame shoots from his mouth. Brian just manages to jump out of the way. "I beg your pardon," apologizes the dragon in his normal voice. "Hooray, it was dragon's fire!" cries the spider. "Am I really better?" the dragon asks Brian. Brian nods his head. "Yes, you're better, thanks to the magic jewel."

24 November

The dragon surprises Brian

The dragon is very happy indeed. "I can breathe dragon fire again!" he cries. "How can I ever thank you?" he asks Brian. "There's nothing to thank us for," Brian replies. "You must thank Wizard Gombal and his magic jewel." The dragon looks disappointed. "I'm so glad I'm better. Just tell me what I can do for you," he insists. Brian ponders for a moment. Then he decides to tell the dragon about the frog princess, trapped in the Dragon's Pool. "Oh, I can certainly help you, then," cries the dragon. "I am the keeper of the animals magicked to Dragon's Valley. I take care of them and make sure they don't escape!"

Endora shows her hand

"The keeper? Escape?" cries Brian in horror. "Are you the creature of that wicked witch Endora?" he demands sternly. "Oh no, not at all," stammers the dragon. "I may have been once, but not any more. You are my best friends now," he continues. "I didn't realize she was wicked. She told me she only cast her spells on disobedient animals, and sent them here for a while." Mr Crackers feels sorry for the dragon. "She played a rotten trick on you," he replies. "Yes, but now I know better. Please don't be angry with me," implores the dragon. The two friends reassure the dragon. It was all the fault of that wicked witch Endora.

Where is everyone?

The next morning, the dragon is feeling himself again. "Of course I can take you to the frog princess!" he cries. Brian and Mr Crackers say goodbye to the spider, and set off for the Dragon's Pool. It seems as though Dragon Valley has died, because everything is so still. "Where *is* everyone?" Brian asks the dragon. "The animals hide when they hear me coming," the dragon replies shyly. "I must tell them not to be frightened." Mr Crackers flaps his wings. "I can do that for you," he says, and he flies on ahead to give the animals the good news.

27 November

The animals don't believe me!

There's no one to be seen when Brian and the dragon arrive at the Dragon Pool. "Look, there's Mr Crackers," cries Brian. "Perhaps he can tell us what's happening." Mr Crackers lands on Brian's shoulder. "The animals don't believe me. They think Endora is up to her tricks again," he tells the bear. The dragon looks sad. "Oh dear, what can we do?" he asks Brian. "Frogs never stray far from water. The princess must be hiding in the pool," he answers. Brian cups his paws around his mouth. "Don't be afraid of us, frog princess," he calls. "We've come to take you home!" Nothing ruffles the still water. Then the friends hear a gentle croak, and a little frog leaves her hiding place, under a lily pad in the pool.

217

28 November

Found at last

The frog princess swims towards Brian. "Can I trust the dragon?" she whispers in her gentle voice. Brian smiles at the princess. "I promise you he's changed," he replies. "He's your loyal friend." The dragon bows his head. He doesn't want flames shooting out of his mouth and frightening the animals again. The frog princess hops onto the grass, and then she jumps into Brian's palm. "I'm so glad we've found you at last," says Brian. "Now we can all go home." "*Croak*!" and another frog joins the princess. "This is my friend," explains the frog princess, blushing a little. "He wants to come home, too."

29 November

Some of the animals want to stay behind

It isn't long before the rest of the animals join the frog princess. They're still rather scared of the dragon, but when they see he's trying his hardest to be friendly, they soon start to relax and settle down. "My goodness!" exclaims Mr Crackers. "I didn't realize there were so many of you." Brian looks thoughtful. "I hope we'll find enough magic pondweed to get us home." Molly the mole puts his mind at rest. "Some of us have decided we would rather stay," she says. "We can be happy here, now we're not afraid of the dragon." The dragon looks really pleased. "Oh! That's so nice of you," he cries. "I'll look after you all, and make sure you never come to harm." And he shoots a little flame into the air because he's so excited.

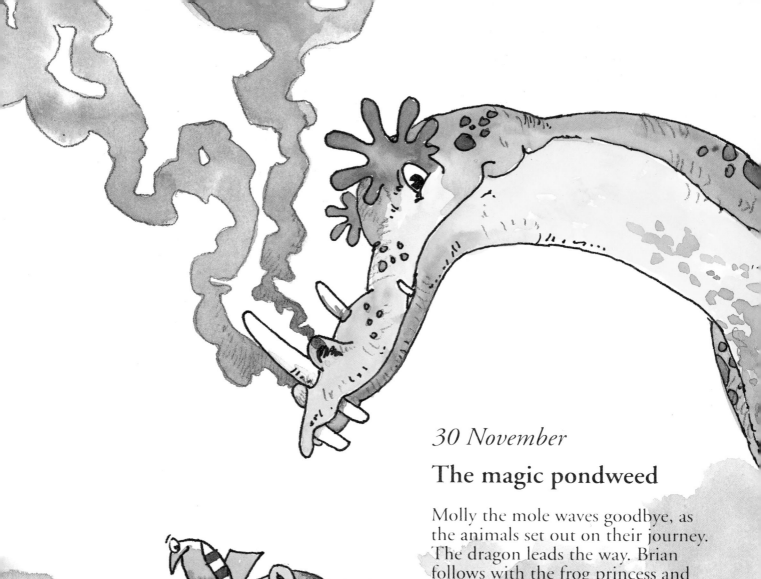

30 November

The magic pondweed

Molly the mole waves goodbye, as the animals set out on their journey. The dragon leads the way. Brian follows with the frog princess and her friend on one shoulder, and with Mr Crackers on the other. Last of all, comes Penny and Danny the mice, and Diana the deer. "How far do we have to go?" Brian asks the dragon. "We're almost there," the dragon reassures him. "Look, there's the pondweed bush," he says, pointing to a little shrub growing close to a pool. The bush is covered with yellow berries. "The juice of those berries will give you magical powers," the dragon tells Brian. Brian picks enough berries to give a handful to everyone. "Don't squeeze the berries until you're ready to pass through the fourth door," the dragon warns them.

1 December

The pondweed bush

A single plant called the pondweed bush
Can help Brian and all his friends.
This enchanted shrub grows by a pool,
With the power their ills to mend.
Soon it is time to squeeze the fruit,
And take us to our journey's end.

2 December

The fourth door

"Where *is* the fourth door?" Brian asks the dragon.
"Just in front of you," the dragon replies.
Brian turns round. "Look, Mr Crackers!"
he cries. "It's just like the door that led us into
'nowhere' land." Everyone has fallen silent.
Can this really be the fourth door?
Can they go home to the Misty Forest
at last? Will they see their families and
friends? They all walk towards the
door and Brian grabs hold of the handle.
Everyone holds their breath in anticipation.

3 December

The door won't open

Brian turns the handle. Nothing happens. He pushes against the door with all his strength, but still nothing happens. The dragon tries to help. He thrusts his powerful shoulders against the door, but *still* nothing happens. "How can we open this door?" asks Brian with a sob. Tears run down the frog princess's face. "I so wanted to see my mother and father again," she weeps. Everyone tries to console her, but her tears run even faster. Brian gives her a hug and produces the large red handkerchief that Captain Ironhook gave him. "Don't cry," he comforts her. "We'll think of something."

4 December

I know just what to do

"Can't we go *round* the door?" asks Diana. "No, you can't," the dragon replies sadly. "The magic juice won't work unless you go through the door. If you don't go *through* the door, you'll be trapped for ever in 'nowhere' land." Mr Crackers starts to flutter his wings in excitement. "Yippee! I've got it!" he cries. "I know just what to do to solve the problem."

222

5 December

The dragon to the rescue

"You can help us," says Mr Crackers, looking straight at the dragon. "But what can *I* do?" asks the dragon, looking puzzled. "I've already tried to break down the door, but I couldn't move it." Mr Crackers jumps up and down in excitement. "What about burning a hole in it?" he asks the dragon. "Of course, that's it!" cries Brian. "How clever of you, Mr Crackers!" The frog princess dries her eyes. "Please help us," she begs the dragon. "I'll certainly try," the dragon replies, as he walks up to the door. "Stand back everybody!"

6 December

Success at last!

The dragon takes a deep breath, and puffs as hard as he can. Flames come shooting out of his mouth. When the smoke clears, the animals can see a large hole burnt in the door. "Hooray! It's worked," everyone cheers. "Now we can go home." The frog princess smiles at last. "Can we leave at once?" she asks. "Yes, of course we can, but we must say goodbye to the dragon," says Mr Crackers. The princess hops over to the dragon. "I'll never forget you," she says, as she kisses his enormous nose. "Thank you for all you've done."

7 December

Whosh! Whosh! Whosh!

At last, the time has arrived for the animals to leave 'nowhere' land. "I think we're ready," cries Brian. "Goodbye, Dragon!" Brian steps through the fourth door and squeezes the magic berries. Everything turns black. Brian is helter-skeltering through space. *Whosh!* his feet suddenly touch the ground. *Whosh!* Here's Mr Crackers. *Whosh!* Here's the frog princess. *Whosh! Whosh! Whosh!* the other animals appear, one by one. Everyone holds their breath. Yippee! This is the Misty Forest.

8 December

Back in the Misty Forest

"Hooray, we're home!" cries Penny the mouse. "Look, Danny, there's our hedgerow." Everyone is so happy to be in the Misty Forest again. "I'll take you to your parents now," Brian tells the frog princess. He gathers the princess and her friend in his paw, and places them on his shoulder. Brian smiles at Penny and Danny. "Watch out for Endora, don't let her catch you again." Suddenly, the animals feel scared. "I'd forgotten about the witch," cries Diana. Brian hates seeing his friends look frightened. "Don't be afraid. If I have anything to do with it, she won't be around much longer!"

9 December

We're not leaving you on your own!

The frog princess glances at Diana. Then she jumps down from Brian's shoulder and hops over to join Penny and Danny. The animals put their heads together, and start whispering to each other. Brian is puzzled. He stares at Mr Crackers with a question in his eyes, but his friend just shrugs his shoulders. After a while, the animals come over to join Brian and Mr Crackers. "You rescued us all from 'nowhere' land," Diana tells Brian. "We're going to help you get rid of Endora. We're not leaving you on your own!"

10 December

She won't leave us in peace

Brian doesn't know what to say. Of course he wants to get rid of Endora, but he'd hoped to see Miss Peggy first. She could help him with her magic. "Can't I take you to your family?" he asks the frog princess. Brian has to take the princess back to her parents before he can return to Miss Peggy. "Oh no," the frog princess replies. "We *must* do something about Endora. When she finds out that we're back, she won't leave us in peace." Mr Crackers whispers in Brian's ear. "That's what happens when you're a hero. It's a good thing you've got that magic jewel that Wizard Gombal gave you."

11 December

You lead the way, Diana

The magic jewel! Brian had forgotten all about it. He gives Mr Crackers a huge smile. He doesn't need Miss Peggy now because he can manage without her. Danny and Penny are getting impatient. Why is Brian hesitating? There's no time to lose when you're up against Endora. Brian makes a move at last. "Okay," he cries. "Let's deal with that wicked witch Endora!" He places the frog princess and her friend back on his shoulder. "You can lead the way," Brian tells Diana.

12 December

Quick, hide!

Brian is deep in thought as he follows Diana along the path to the witch's house. How can he use the magic jewel against Endora? There must be something he can do, but what? Suddenly the animals hear a rumbling noise echoing from the sky above them. "Quick, hide!" cries Mr Crackers. "It's Endora! She's out on her broomstick!" The animals rush away to hide. Brian tries to make himself scarce as he cowers behind a tree trunk. He's frightened of the witch's sharp eyes. There she is! Has she spotted the animals?

13 December

Have they been spotted?

The animals hold their breath. Penny and Danny shut their eyes because they're so scared. At last the rumbling noise moves away. In a short while everything is silent. No one dares move. At last they hear Mr Crackers' voice. "You can come out now," he whispers. Diana looks at Brian with her big brown eyes. "Do you think she saw us?" she asks. "No, I don't think so," replies the bear. "She wouldn't have flown away if she'd spotted us." The animals want to believe him, but when they set off again they keep looking round nervously.

14 December

I must be mistaken

Endora lands the broomstick on her lawn. She strides into the house, slamming the front door behind her. Then she marches into the kitchen and flops into a chair. Her cat, Bobby, looks at his mistress in surprise. "It isn't possible," she mutters to herself. "I must be mistaken." Bobby rubs his head against Endora's leg, and looks at her inquiringly. "Do you know who I've seen, Bobby?" Endora asks sharply. Bobby shakes his head. "That stupid bear and his friend, the little bird." What? Bobby stares at his mistress in disbelief, and his tail stands on end.

15 December

I can see everything

"It's not just the bear and his friend," Endora continues. "But lots of the animals I sent to 'nowhere' land. They were trying to hide from *me*!" and she laughs menacingly. Her laughter makes Bobby wince. "Those animals didn't know I was wearing my special glasses," she cries. "I can see *everything*!" Endora scowls. "I'll catch them again, soon. And I'll punish that stupid dragon. It's all his fault. It's time he was taught a lesson!" the wicked witch mutters to herself, as she thumbs through her book, looking for a spell to punish the dragon with.

16 December

Let's put it to the test

Ha, ha, ha, ha! I'll have them soon.
They won't escape from me.
The bear, the bird and all their friends
Won't have the victory.

Ha, ha, ha, ha! I'll have them soon.
Till then I will not rest.
He who laughs last, laughs longest,
So let's put it to the test.

17 December

Be careful!

The animals stop in their tracks when they see the witch's house looming
through the trees. Brian doesn't know what to do, so he looks at Mr Crackers.
"I think I've got a plan," the bird whispers in Brian's ear.
"Give me the magic jewel." Brian looks horrified. "Give *you* the magic jewel?"
he asks. "How can I protect myself from Endora?"
Mr Crackers looks furious. "I'm the one with a plan, not you.
Don't be so selfish!" Brian blushes with shame, and gives his friend
the magic jewel. "Good luck," he whispers as Mr Crackers flies off towards
the witch's house. "Be careful!"

18 December

Like a rocket

Bobby is sitting by the window. Suddenly, he spots Mr Crackers flying towards the house. He hisses and runs out of the kitchen. Then he claws at the front door, meowing frantically. "Now what's the matter?" grumbles Endora. She opens the front door and looks out. And what does she see? Mr Crackers flying straight at her. "Aha!" she cries. "I've got you!" and she jumps onto her broomstick. Bobby skips on behind her. But what's happening? The broomstick takes off like a rocket into the sky. Up and up it goes! Endora and Bobby cling on for dear life. The witch shrieks every spell she knows, but the broomstick keeps rocketing into the heavens. Suddenly, there's a flash of light and the broomstick vanishes!

19 December

Mr Crackers is a hero

"They've gone!" the animals cry in delight. "They've vanished!" The princess hugs Mr Crackers. "You're a hero," she says, and gives him a kiss. Brian looks at his friend. "How did you do it?" he asks. "I hid the magic jewel in the broomstick," Mr Crackers replies. "I knew Endora would use it. The jewel certainly did its work," he continues. "We won't be troubled by that witch again!" Everyone looks at Mr Crackers in awe. What a brave bird he is, and so clever. "But you shouldn't just thank me," says Mr Crackers. "If Brian hadn't lent me the magic jewel, it would never have happened." The princess gives the bear a hug. "Thank you, Brian," she says in her gentle voice. Mr Crackers winks at his friend. "What a pal you are," thinks Brian.

20 December

Let's give them a surprise

Brian, Mr Crackers and all the animals joyfully set off for the great lake, where the frog king holds his court among the bulrushes. "Shall I fly on ahead and give your parents the good news?" Mr Crackers asks the frog princess. The princess thinks for a moment. "No, let's give them a surprise," she says.

21 December

Ferdie, the frog

Shortly after Brian and Mr Crackers set off on their journey to rescue the frog princess, the frog king decided to put a sentry on duty to watch for their return. Today, it's Ferdie the frog's turn to stand lookout on the little hill. He has almost lost hope of seeing his princess again. "Where are you Brian?" he groans. But what's that? Ferdie raises his head. It sounds like singing. He peers into the distance. Who are those animals dancing, hopping, and skipping towards him? Ferdie blinks and looks again. Isn't that Brian? Ferdie's heart leaps and almost bursts with joy when he sees the princess sitting on Brian's shoulder. Then the frog's heart sinks. What's the special signal he must give to the king? At last he remembers. "Croakety, croak, croakety, croak!" Ferdie shouts at the top of his voice. "Hurrah, our princess is home again!"

22 December

Hip, hip, hooray

The frogs are thrown into turmoil when they hear Ferdie's signal. Is it really true? Can they believe their ears? They rush out of the bulrushes to see what's happening. "There she comes," cry the frogs. "Hip, hip, hooray!" Then there's a tremendous shout. "Long live the princess! Welcome home!" The frog king seizes the frog queen's hand as they wait to greet their daughter. "Mother! Father!" cries the frog princess when she sees her parents. And with one enormous jump, she leaps into their arms. "I've missed you so much," she cries. "I'm so happy to be back home."

23 December

A double celebration

That evening, a fantastic party is held in the Misty Forest to celebrate the victory over the wicked witch Endora, and to greet all the animals who have come back home. Brian and Mr Crackers are the heroes of the hour. Everyone makes a tremendous fuss of them. It's very late when Brian hears a familiar voice behind him. "Hello hero! Don't you think it's time for *you* to go home?" Brian turns and sees Miss Peggy. "Oh, Miss Peggy! How lovely to see you again!" he cries, as he gives her a great hug in the way bears do. "I've been waiting for you to return," Miss Peggy tells Brian. "I'm *really* proud of you both. Mustardseed told me the good news this evening!"

24 December

It's winter again

All the animals in the Misty Forest are sad Brian and Mr Crackers have to leave them so soon. "Come back in the spring for the royal wedding," smiles the frog king, as he watches his daughter dancing with her loyal friend. After they have all said goodbye, Brian, Mr Crackers and Miss Peggy set out for her cottage. "It's certainly time we were getting back to *our* forest," says Miss Peggy. "Winter's setting in. If we wait much longer, my cottage won't be able to fly us home." Brian looks around in surprise. Yes, the trees are all bare. What a long time they've been away!

25 December

Another party

Luckily, the wind is blowing in the right direction when Miss Peggy's flying cottage takes off next morning. The first snowflakes are beginning to fall on the landscape beneath them. Brian presses his nose against the window. How lovely it is to see those familiar places again. "There's Farmer George's farm," cries Mr Crackers. "Look at all those animals down there! What's going on?" Miss Peggy smiles. "They're celebrating the coming of winter," she says. "Oh yes, the great Green Tree Festival!" murmurs Brian. "Are you ready for another party?" asks Miss Peggy, as she settles her house into exactly the same spot it had been last winter.

26 December

Icicle is back

Brian opens the front door of the cottage and steps outside. Then he shuts his eyes and takes a deep breath. "Oh, what lovely fresh air!" he exclaims. There's a surprise in store when he opens his eyes. "Hi, Brian!" says a growly voice. "How are you, my friend?" It's Icicle the polar bear, arriving for his annual visit. "Icicle! How lovely to see you again," cries Miss Peggy. "Are you coming to Farmer George's party?" asks Mr Crackers. And it's not long before the friends are on their way to Farmer George's farm.

27 December

The Green Tree Festival

The Green Tree Festival is in full swing.
Farmer George has set up an enormous tree
in the middle of his farmyard. It's
beautifully decorated with golden
pine cones and lit by a hundred candles.
Farmer George has baked lots of cakes and
everyone is sitting happily, enjoying
themselves singing along with the
music. "Mmmm!" cries Brian.
"Cakes made by Farmer George himself.
They're bound to be delicious."
Suddenly all the animals fall silent.
Everyone turns and looks at Brian as
he comes into the farmyard.

28 December

Brian has a story to tell

Farmer George runs up to Brian and gives him a big hug. "Is it really you, Brian?" he
cries happily. "And there's Mr Crackers. Where have you been all this time, my friends?
We thought something dreadful had happened." The animals get over their surprise,
and rush up to the two friends. "Hello, Brian! Hello, Mr Crackers! How lovely to see
you again!" Voices ring out from every side, and Brian has to shake hands with all his
old friends. When things have calmed down a little, Farmer George makes a suggestion.
"I think we'll have a nice long Green Tree story this year," he says. "Yes, please," the
animals cry. "We want Brian to tell us a story!" So Brian begins his adventures. "When
I was disturbed from my winter sleep last year ..."

29 December

The whole night through

Brian has so much to tell his friends, it's a very long story. Whenever he has to pause because his throat is so dry, Mr Crackers takes over. The story telling takes all night, but no one gets bored because it's so exciting. They can't help laughing at Katie, and shuddering when they hear about the dragon. And when Brian tells them how Endora's broomstick shot into space like a rocket, everyone claps and cheers in delight, thumping their fists on the table.

30 December

Who would have thought it?

"And here we are back again," says Brian, as he comes to the end of his tale. Everyone is very impressed. Who would have thought Brian could be so brave? Not to mention Mr Crackers. "I promise not to laugh at you any more," vows Sherman the sheep. "I think we can spare you some honey," promise the bees. "Honey!" cries Brian. "I just love honey!" Everyone laughs. "You haven't changed at all," they chuckle. When it's time to leave, the animals all agree that this was the best Green Tree Festival ever.

31 December

Goodnight, Brian

"Well I don't know about you," Brian announces. "But *I'm* going back to my den for my winter sleep. I think I deserve it!" Brian stifles a yawn. "Can I come and stay with you when I wake up?" he asks Miss Peggy. "Of course you can, Brian," she replies happily. "Could Mr Crackers spend the winter with you, Miss Peggy?" asks Brian. "He gets so lonely without me." Miss Peggy glances at Mr Crackers. "Would you like that, my friend?" she smiles. "Oh, yes please," replies Mr Crackers with a happy grin. "That would be lovely." Brian stifles another yawn. "Well, I'll be off then," he says. "Good night, Brian, sleep well. Until next year!" reply his friends.